Disney
Mega-Hit Movies

D1193180

ISBN 0-634-04514-8

Walt Disney Music Company
Wonderland Music Company, Inc.

DISTRIBUTED BY

HAL•LEONARD®
CORPORATION

7777 W. BLUEMOUND RD. P.O. BOX 13819 MILWAUKEE, WI 53213

Visit Hal Leonard Online at
www.halleonard.com

CONTENTS

FRIEND LIKE ME

from Walt Disney's ALADDIN

Lyrics by HOWARD ASHMAN
Music by ALAN MENKEN

Moderately bright

mf

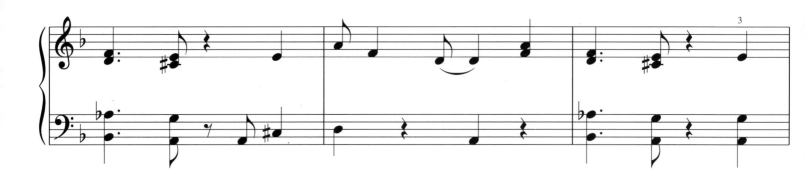

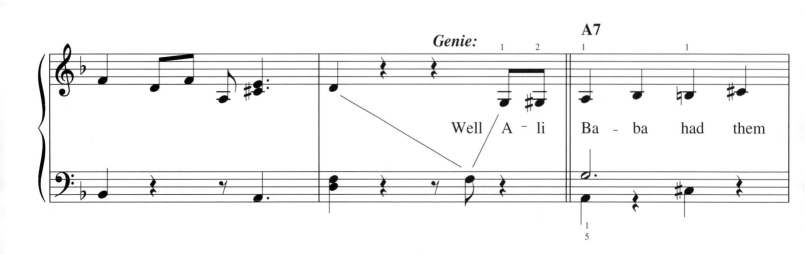

Genie:

A7

Well A - li Ba - ba had them

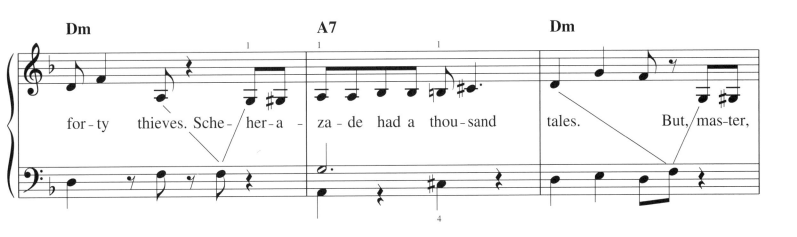

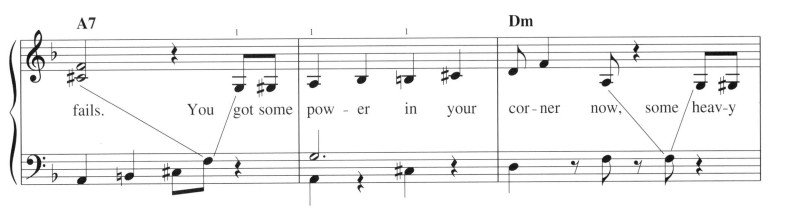

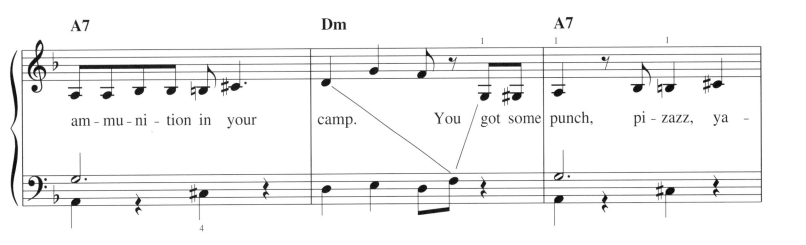

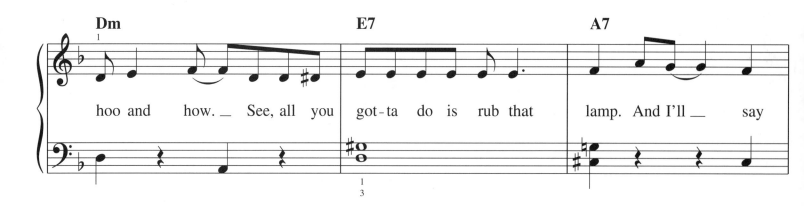

hoo and how. __ See, all you got-ta do is rub that lamp. And I'll __ say

Mis - ter A - lad - din sir, __ what will your plea-sure

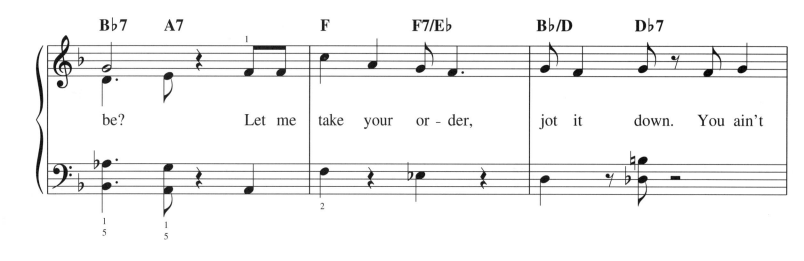

be? Let me take your or-der, jot it down. You ain't

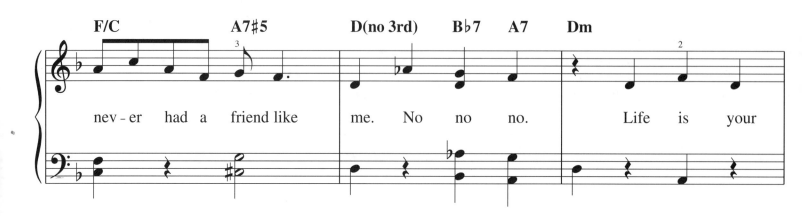

nev - er had a friend like me. No no no. Life is your

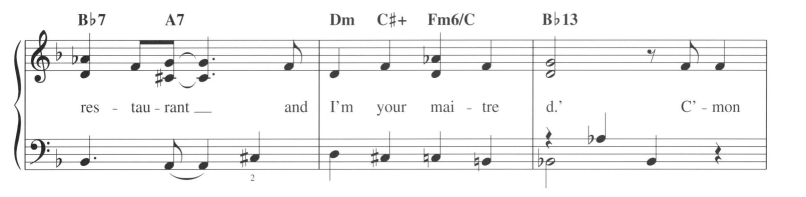

res - tau - rant ___ and I'm your mai - tre d.' C' - mon

whis - per what it is you want. You ain't nev - er had a friend like

me. Yes, sir, we pride our - selves on ser - vice. You're the

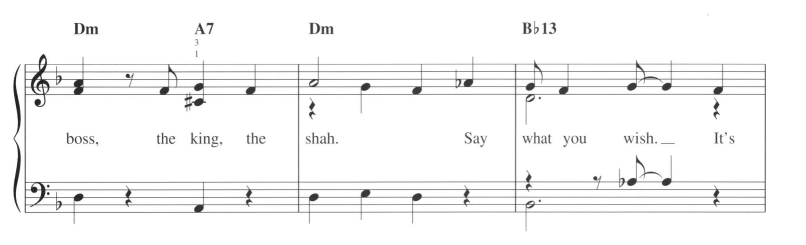

boss, the king, the shah. Say what you wish. ___ It's

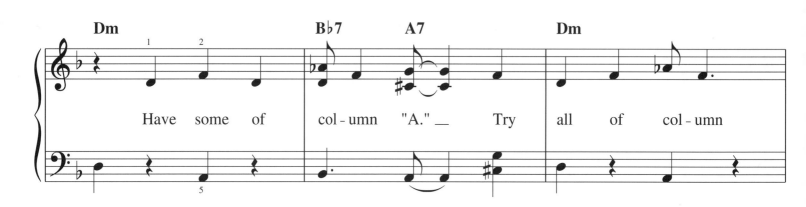

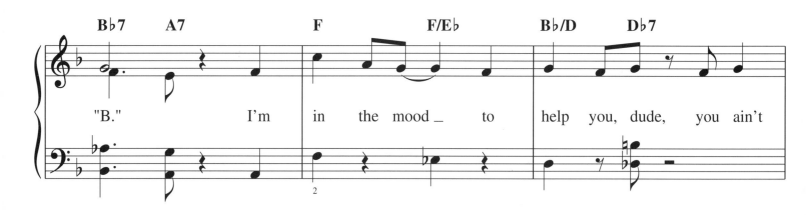

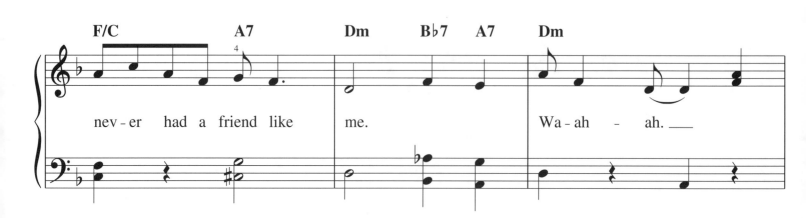

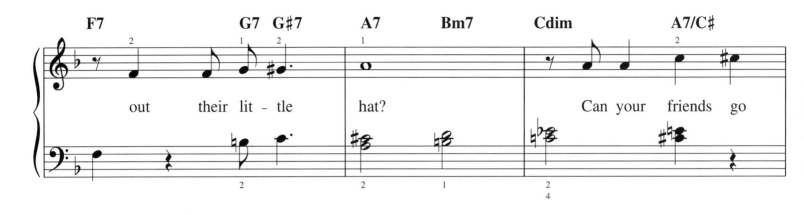

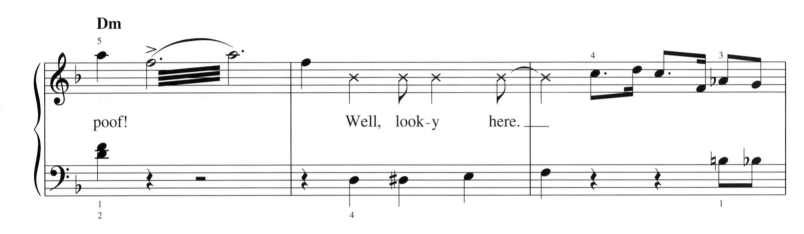

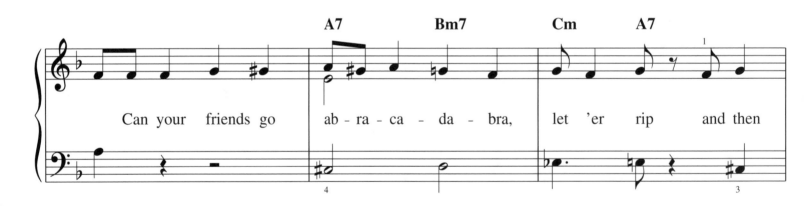

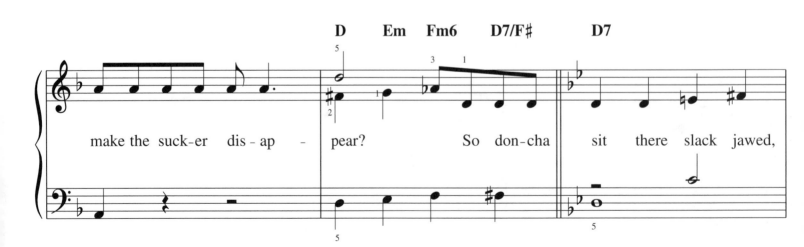

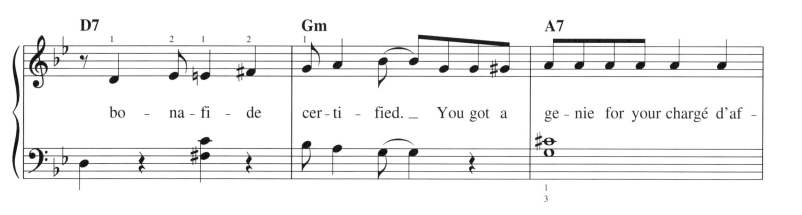
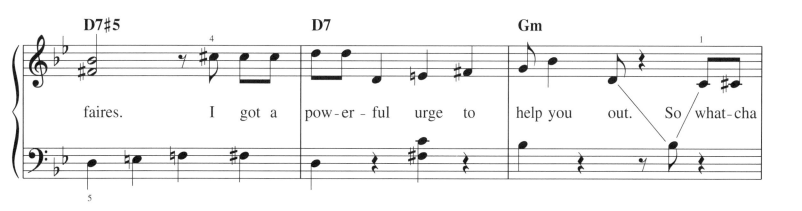
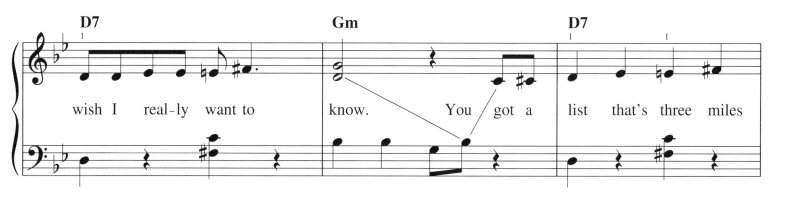

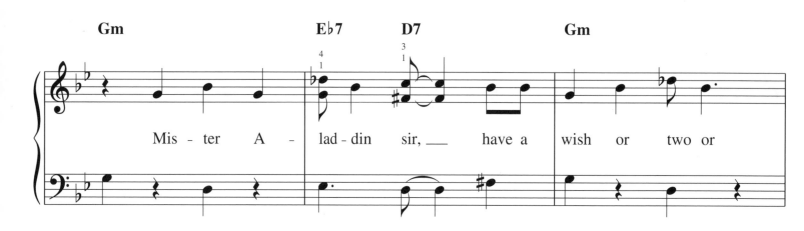

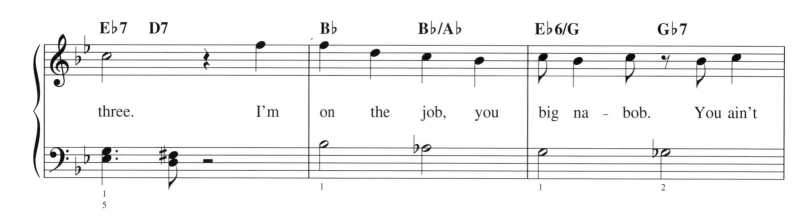

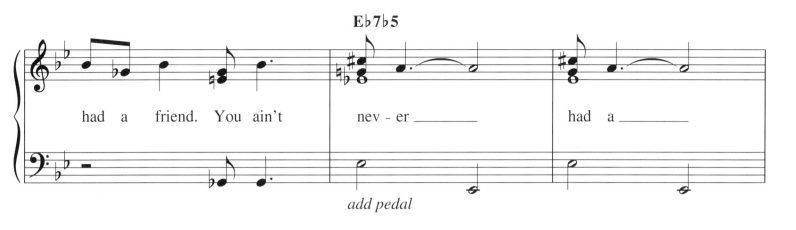

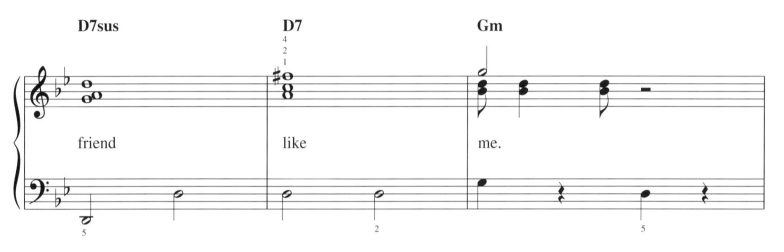

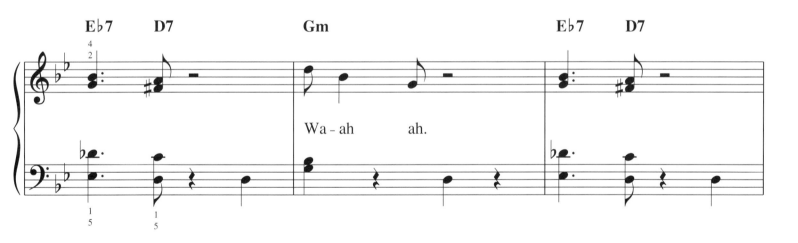

ONE JUMP AHEAD

from Walt Disney's ALADDIN

Music by ALAN MENKEN
Words by TIM RICE

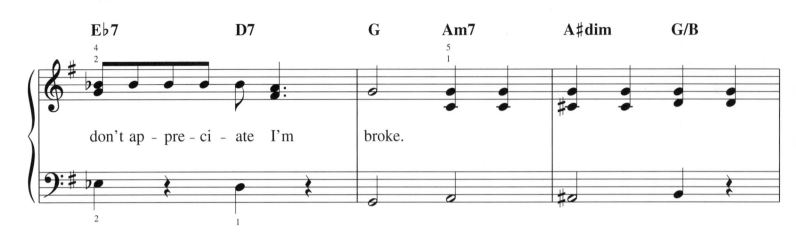

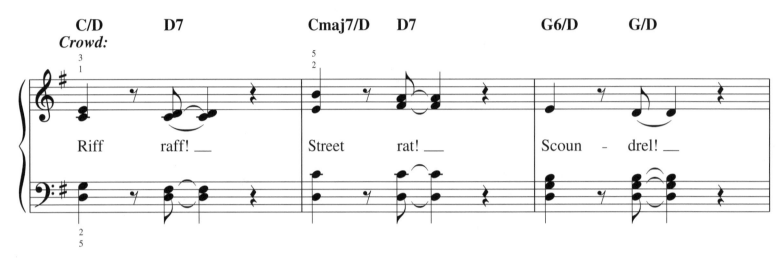

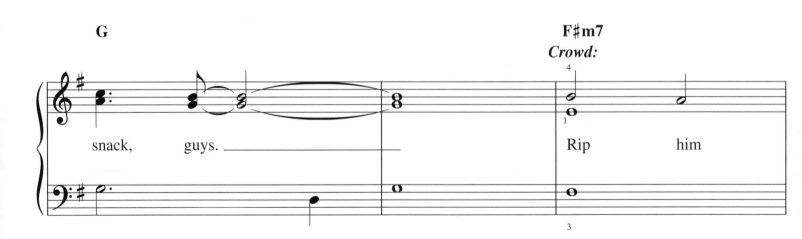

17

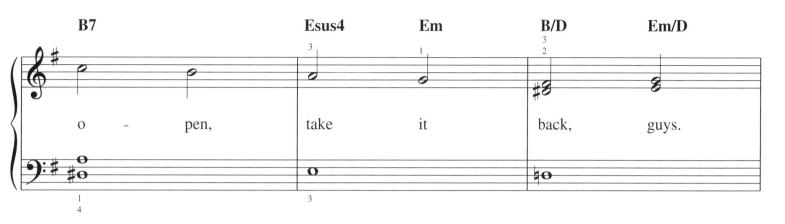

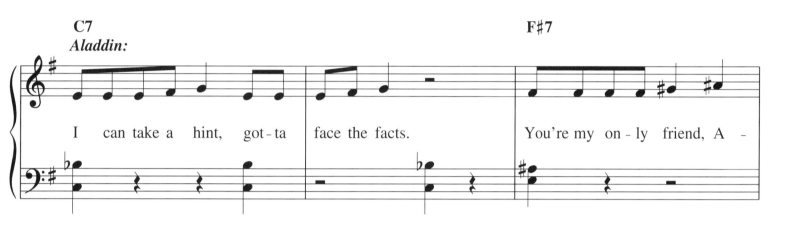

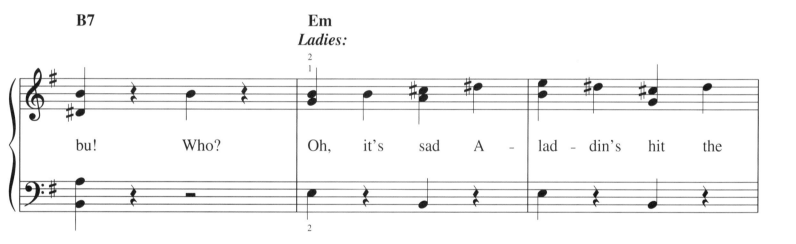

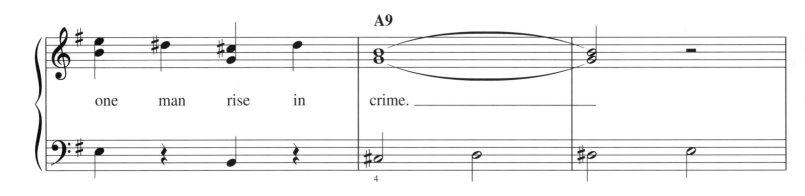

one man rise in crime. _____

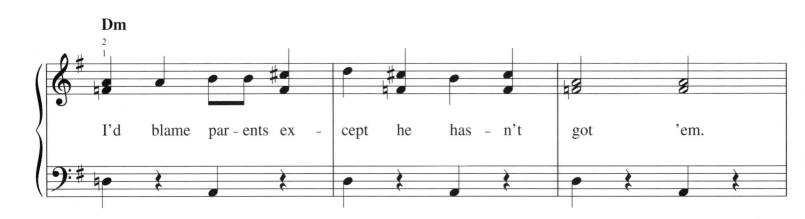

I'd blame par-ents ex - cept he has - n't got 'em.

Aladdin:

Got-ta eat to live, got-ta steal to eat, tell you all a -

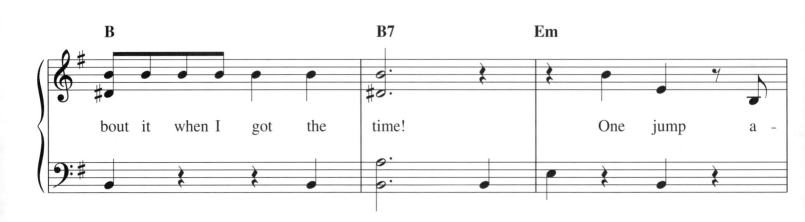

bout it when I got the time! One jump a -

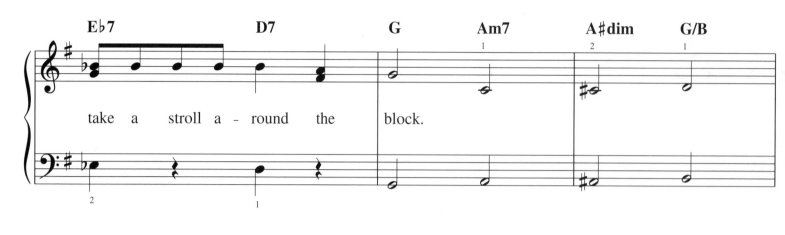

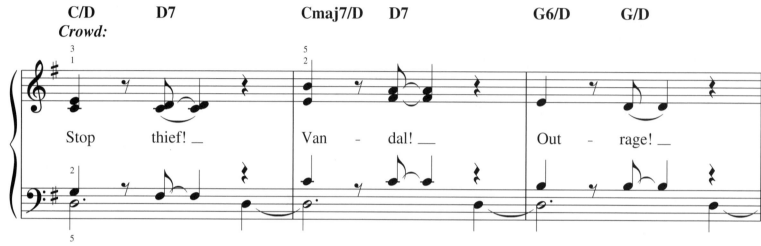

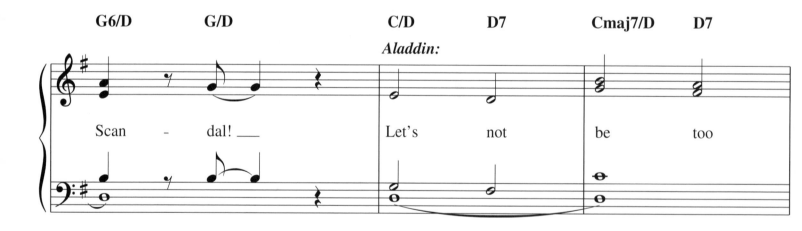

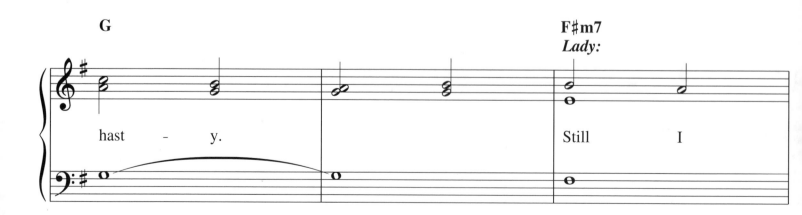

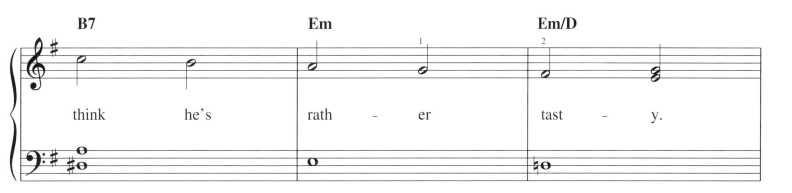

think he's rath – er tast – y.

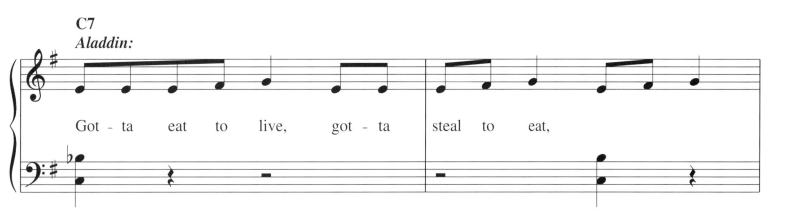

Got – ta eat to live, got – ta steal to eat,

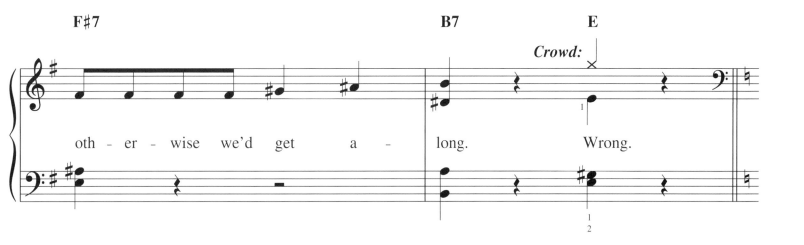

oth – er – wise we'd get a – long. Wrong.

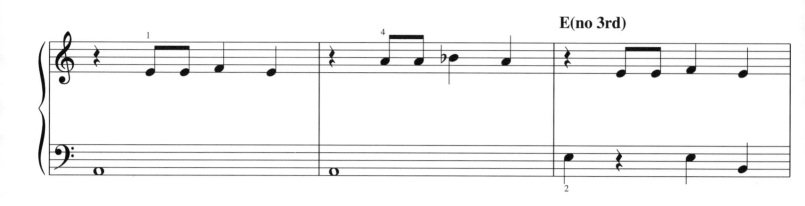

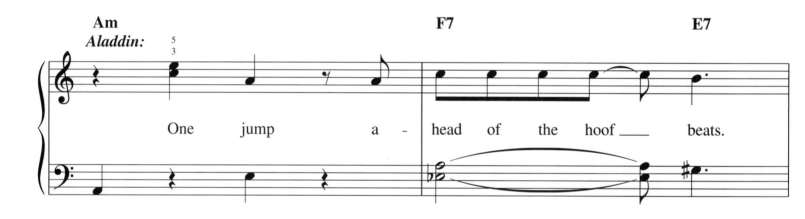

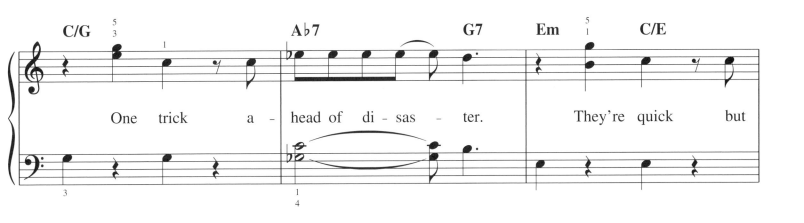

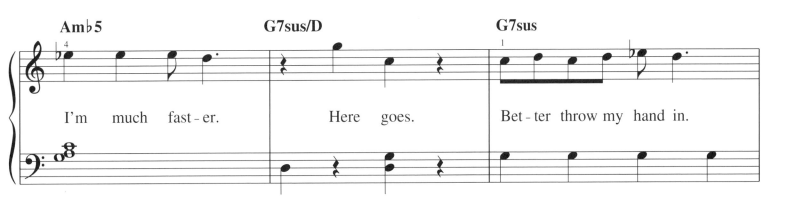

PRINCE ALI

from Walt Disney's ALADDIN

Words by HOWARD ASHMAN
Music by ALAN MENKEN

Moderately slow

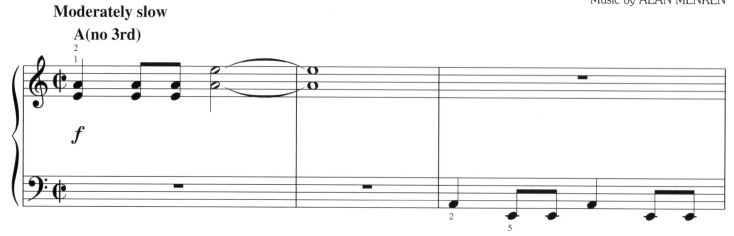

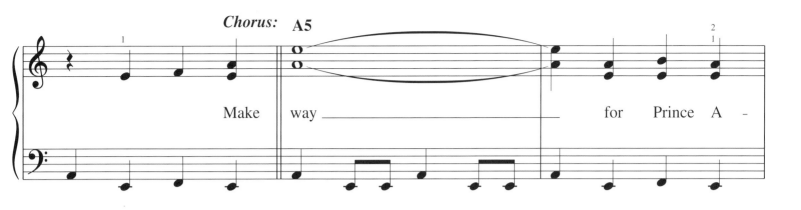

Chorus: **A5**

Make way _____ for Prince A -

li. _____ Say hey, _____

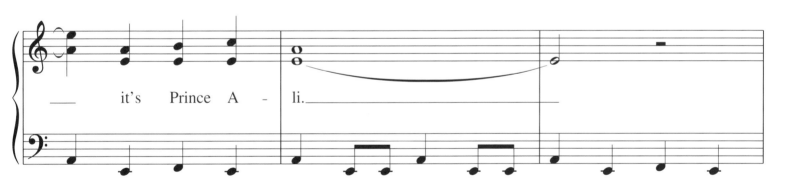

___ it's Prince A - li. _____

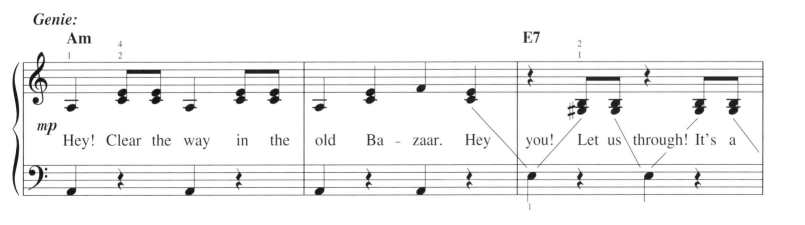

Genie:

Am   **E7**

mp

Hey! Clear the way in the old Ba - zaar. Hey you! Let us through! It's a

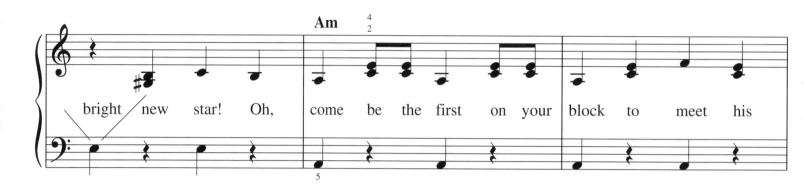

bright new star! Oh, come be the first on your block to meet his

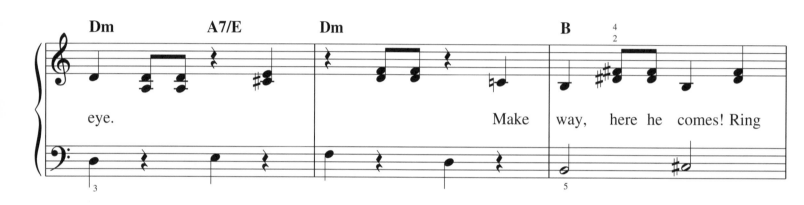

eye. Make way, here he comes! Ring

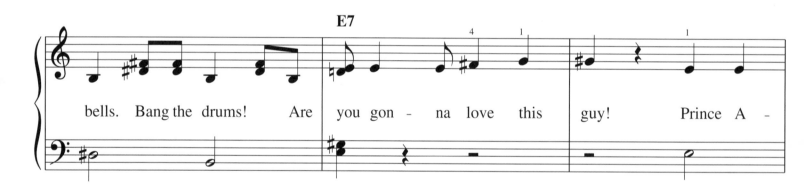

bells. Bang the drums! Are you gon - na love this guy! Prince A -

li! Fab - u - lous he! A - li A - bab - wa.

Gen - u - flect. Show _ some re - spect. Down _ on one

knee! Now try your best _ to stay

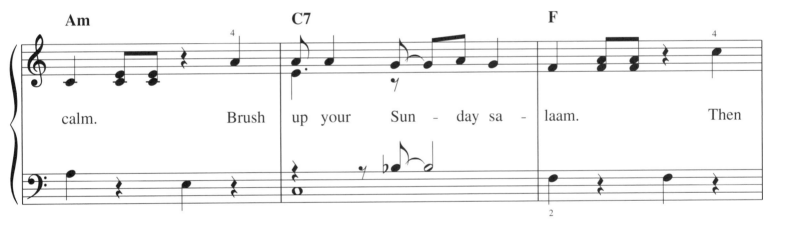

calm. Brush up your Sun - day sa - laam. Then

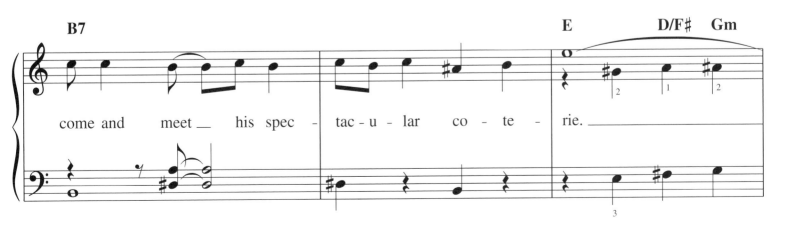

come and meet _ his spec - tac - u - lar co - te - rie. _____

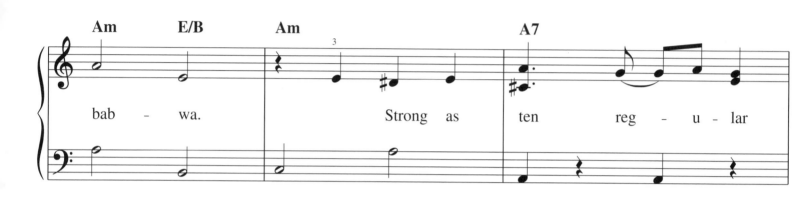

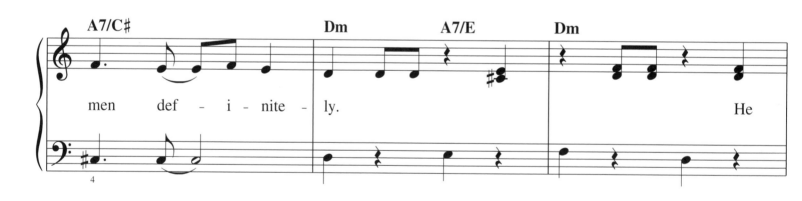

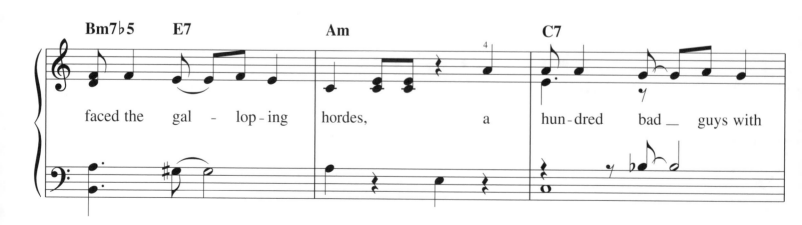

swords. Who sent those goons _ to their Lords? Why Prince A -

li. He's got sev - en - ty

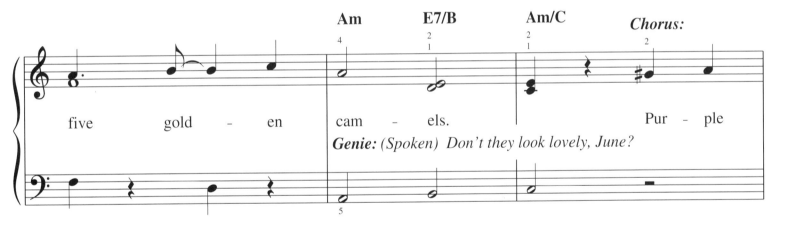

five gold - en cam - els. Pur - ple

Genie: (Spoken) Don't they look lovely, June?

pea - cocks, _ he's got fif - ty - three.

Genie: (Spoken) Fabulous, Harry, I love

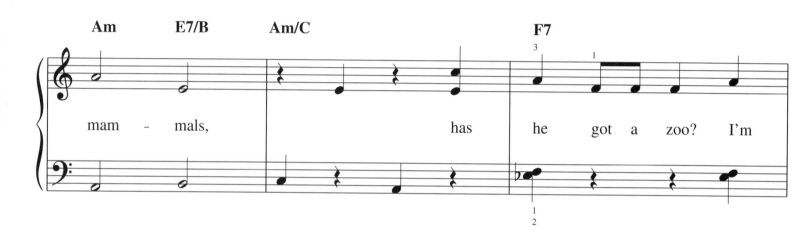

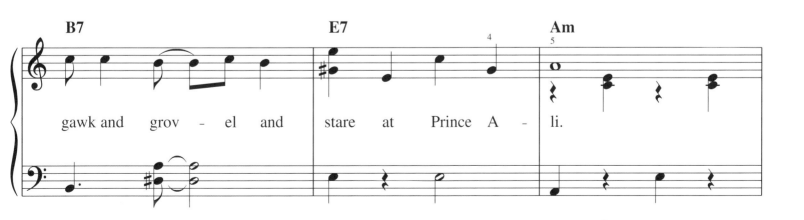

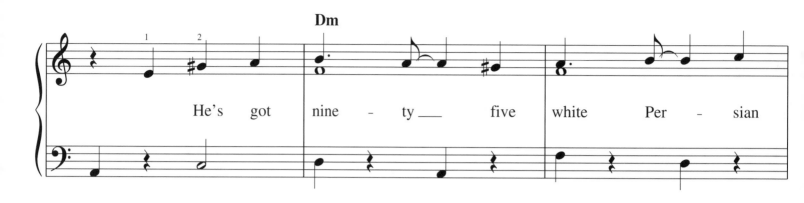

He's got nine - ty ___ five white Per - sian

mon - keys. ___ And to view them ___ he

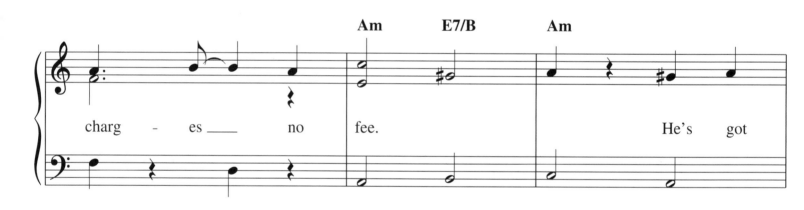

charg - es ___ no fee. He's got

slaves, he's ___ got ser - vants ___ and flun - kies.

Proud to work __ for him, bow to his whim, love serv-ing him. They're just

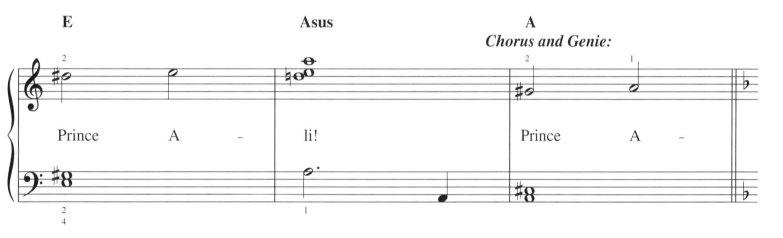

lous-y with loy-al - ty to A - li!

Prince A - li! Prince A -

Chorus and Genie:

li! Am-o-rous he! A - li A-bab - wa. __

34

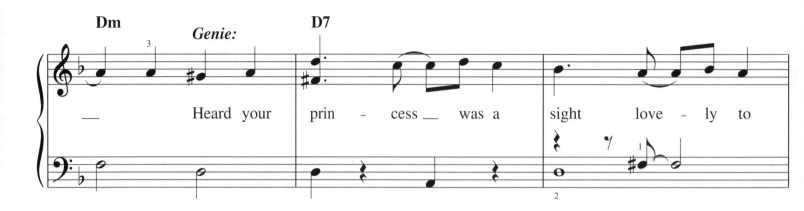

Dm *Genie:* D7

Heard your prin - cess __ was a sight love - ly to

Gm Em7♭5 A7

see. And that, good peo - ple, is

Dm F7 B♭ *Chorus:*

why he got dolled up __ and dropped by with

E7♭9 Gm7

six - ty el - e - phants, lla - mas ga - lore, with his bears and li - ons, a

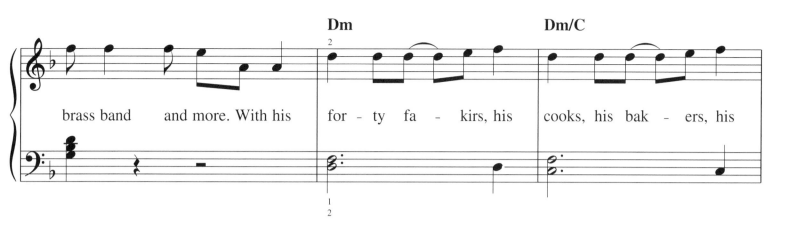

brass band   and more. With his   for - ty fa - kirs, his   cooks, his bak - ers, his

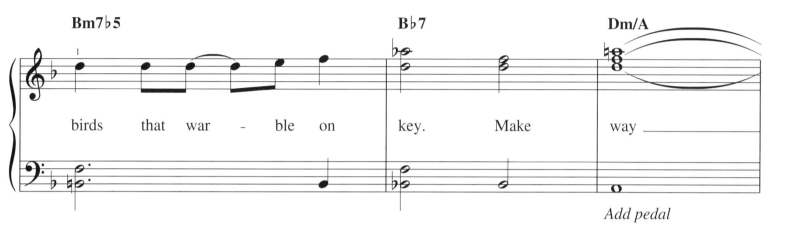

birds   that war - ble on   key.   Make   way _____

Add pedal

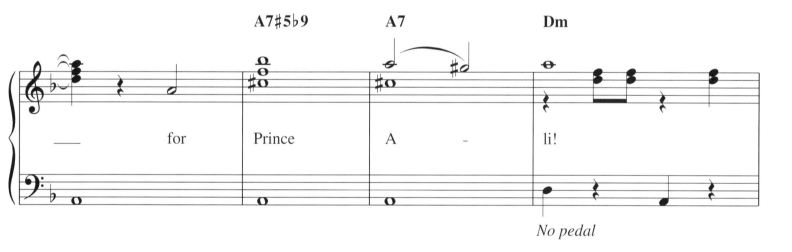

_____   for   Prince   A -   li!

No pedal

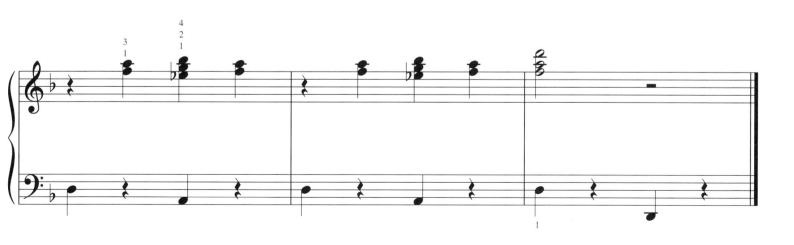

A WHOLE NEW WORLD

from Walt Disney's ALADDIN

Music by ALAN MENKEN
Lyrics by TIM RICE

Slowly and sweetly

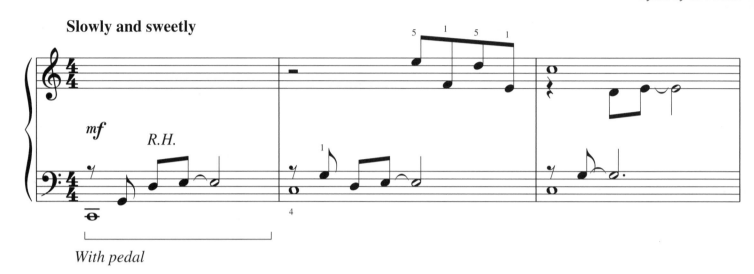

With pedal

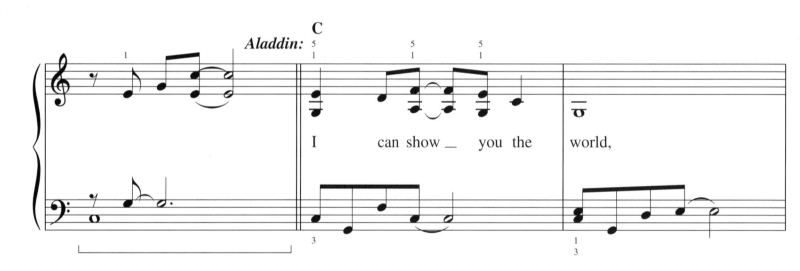

I   can show __ you the   world,

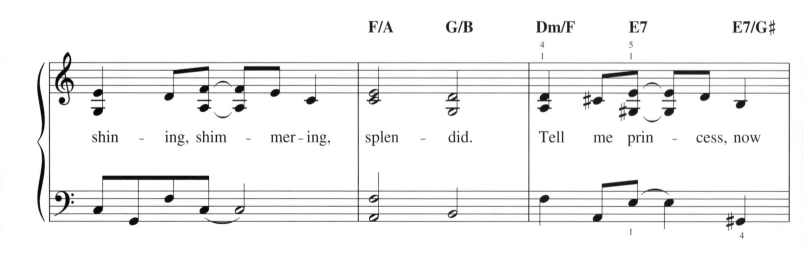

shin - ing, shim - mer - ing,   splen - did.   Tell   me prin - cess, now

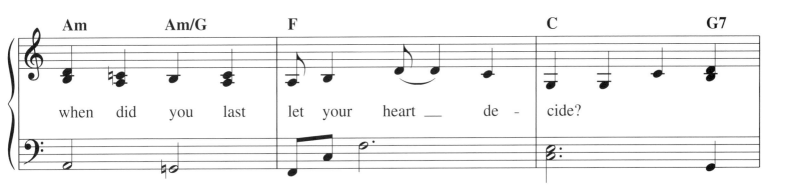

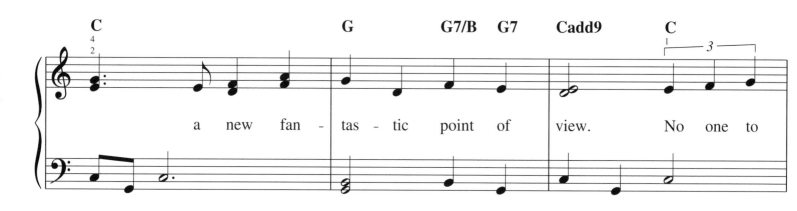

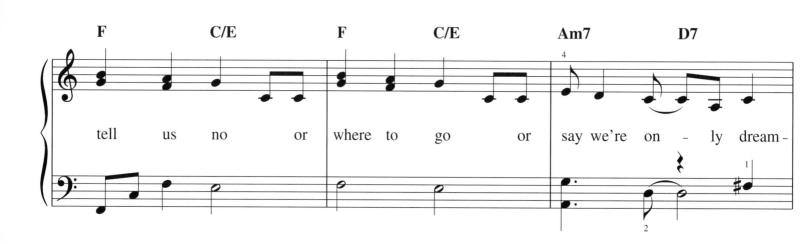

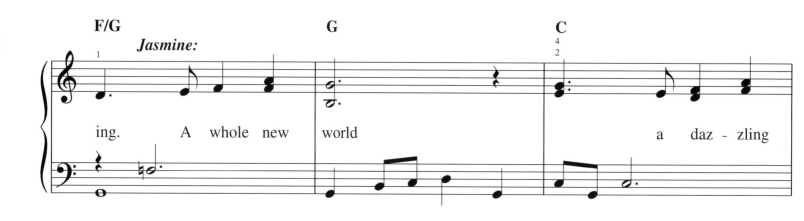

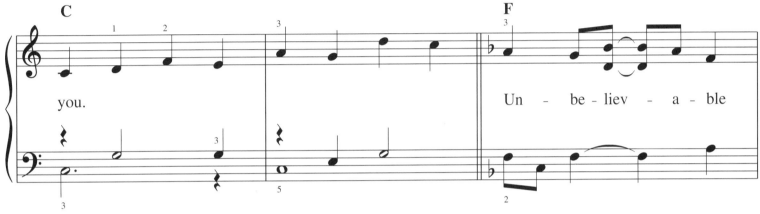

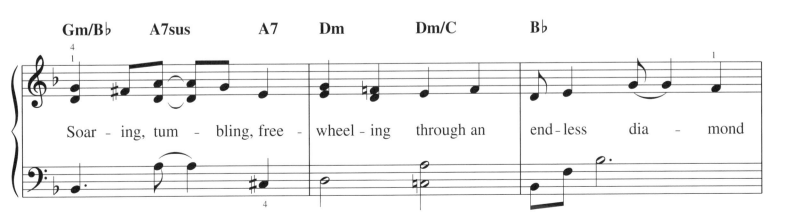

sky.   A whole new world   a hun - dred

thou – sand   things   to   see.   I'm like a

shoot – ing star.   I've   come   so   far   I

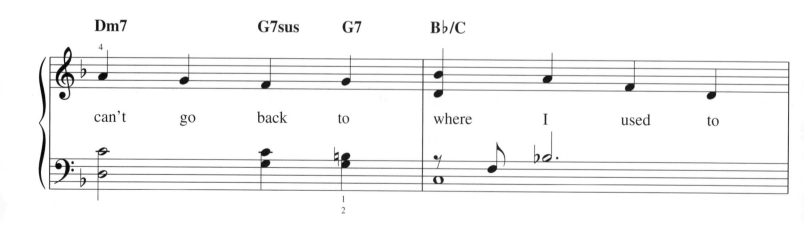

can't   go   back   to   where   I   used   to

41

BE OUR GUEST
from Walt Disney's BEAUTY AND THE BEAST

Lyrics by HOWARD ASHMAN
Music by ALAN MENKEN

Moderately

mf

Lumiere: Ma chere Mademoiselle,

With pedal

it is with deepest pride   and greatest pleasure   that we welcome you   tonight. And now, we

invite you to relax.   Let us pull up a chair as the *rit.*   dining room proudly presents

44

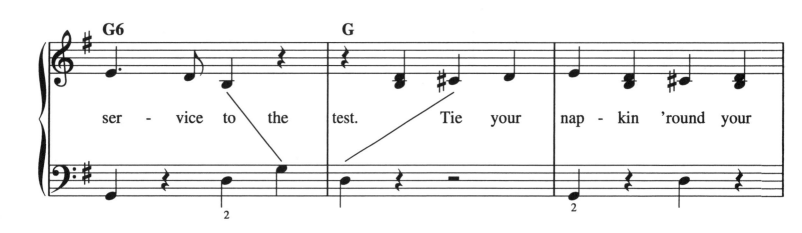

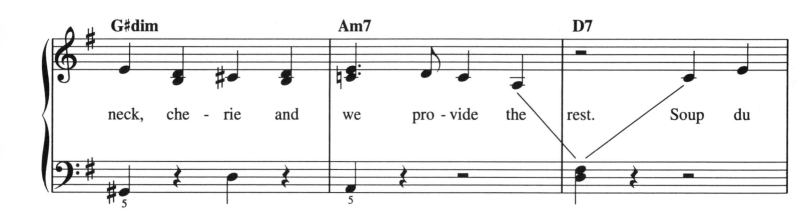

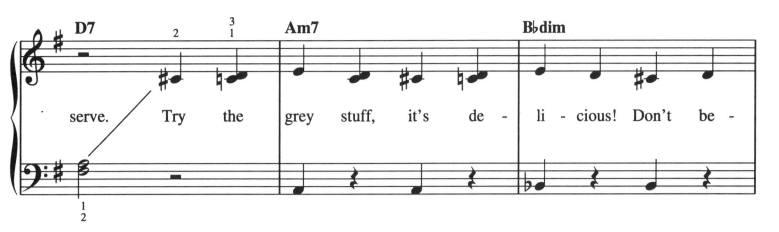

serve. Try the grey stuff, it's de - li - cious! Don't be -

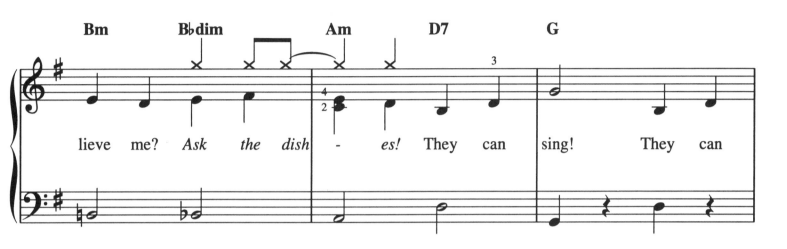

lieve me? *Ask the dish - es!* They can sing! They can

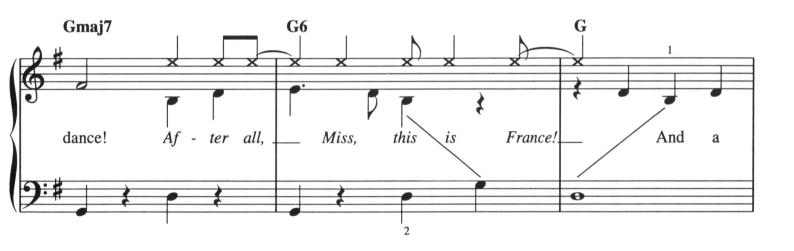

dance! *Af - ter all,* ___ *Miss, this is France!* ___ And a

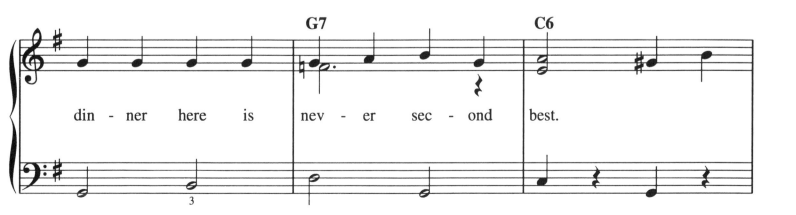

din - ner here is nev - er sec - ond best.

46

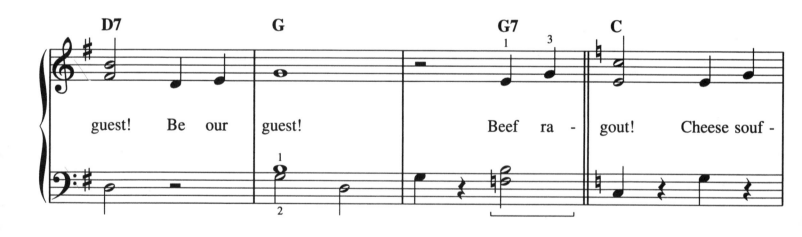

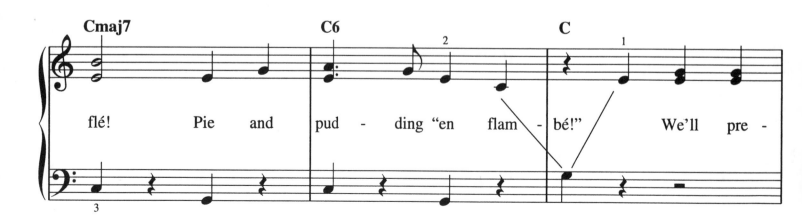

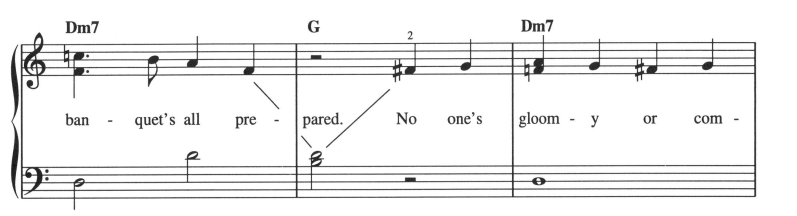

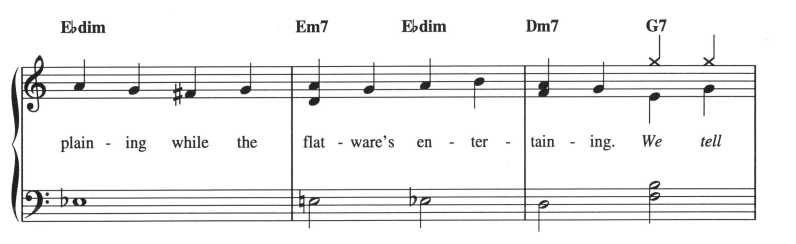

48

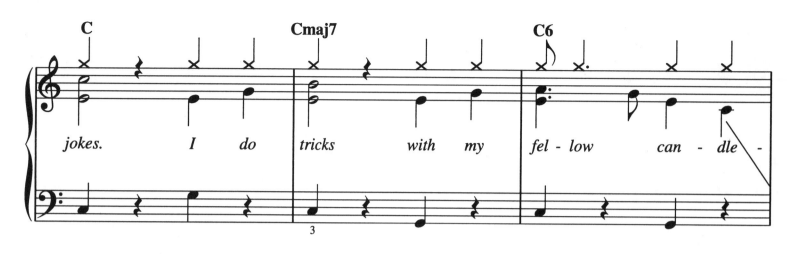

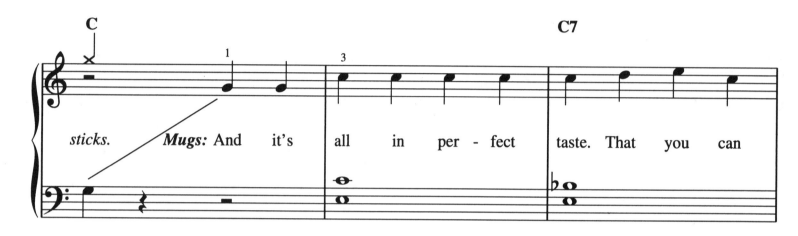

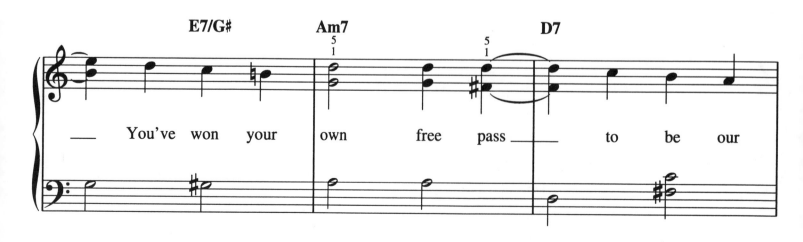

49

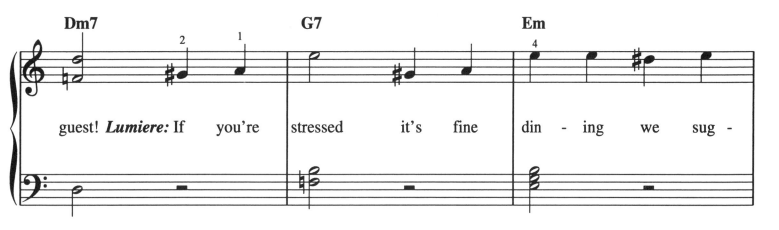

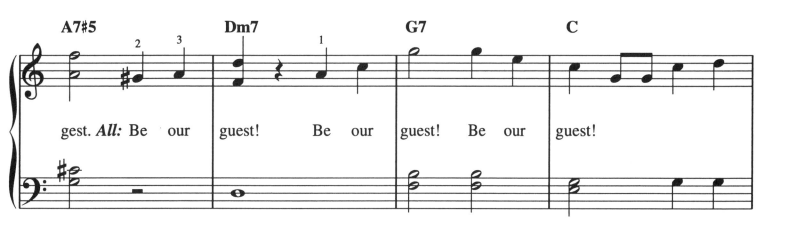

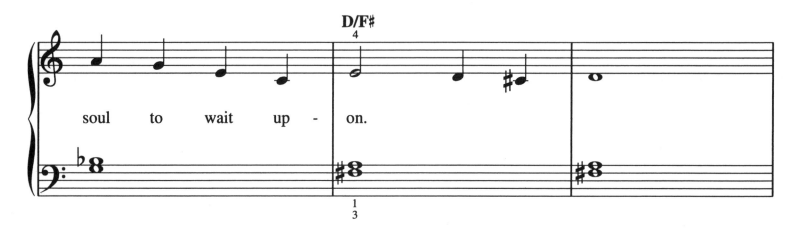

soul   to   wait   up - on.

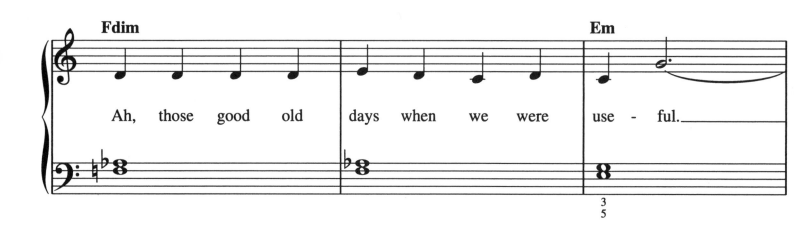

Ah,   those   good   old   days   when   we   were   use - ful._____

_____   Sud - den - ly,   those   good   old   days   are   gone.   *Ten   years,   we've been*

Add pedal

51

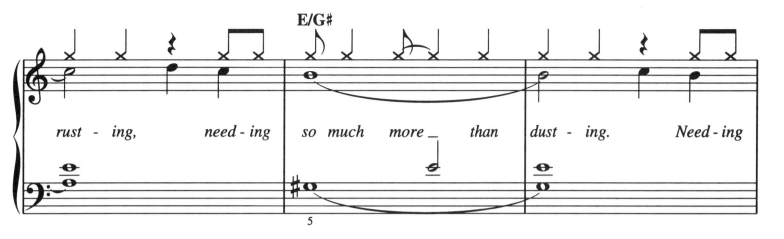

E/G#

rust - ing,   need - ing   so much more ___ than   dust - ing.   Need - ing

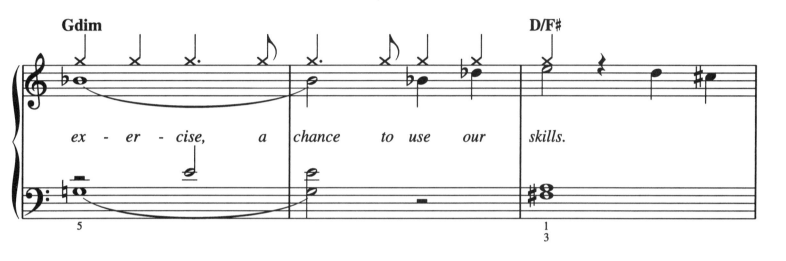

Gdim   D/F#

ex - er - cise,   a   chance   to use   our   skills.

Fdim

Most days,   we   just   lay a - round   the

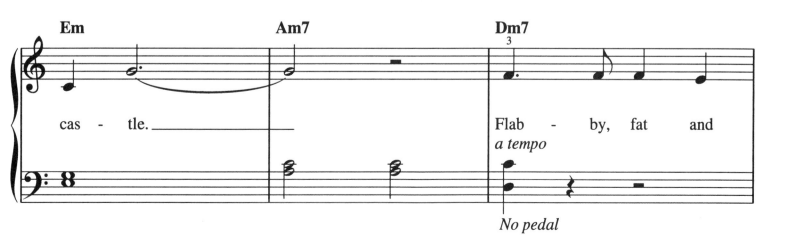

Em   Am7   Dm7

cas - tle. ___   Flab - by, fat   and
                                                   a tempo

No pedal

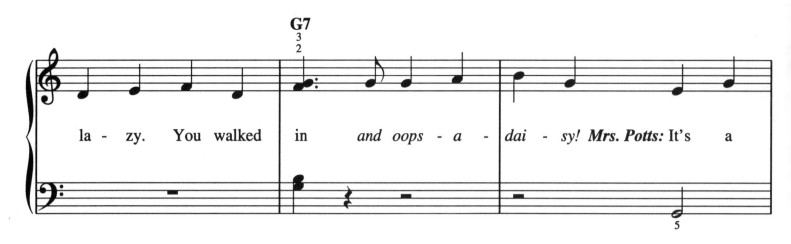

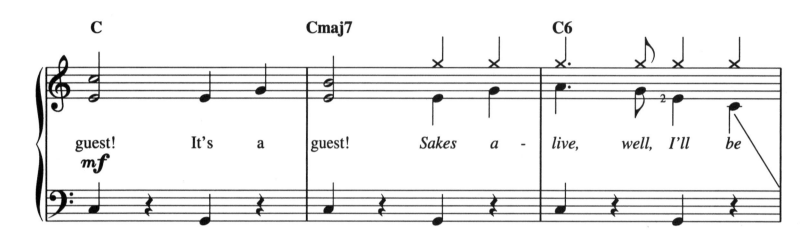

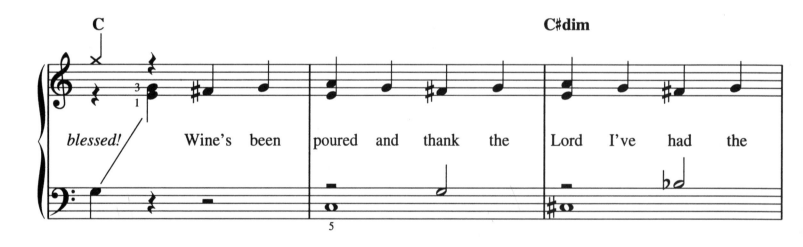

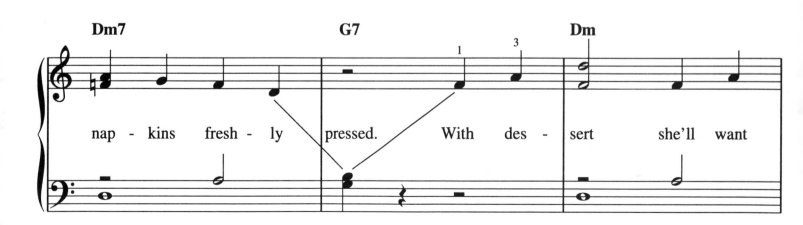

tea. *And my* *dear, that's* *fine with* *me.* While the

cups do their soft shoe - ing, I'll be bub - bling! I'll be

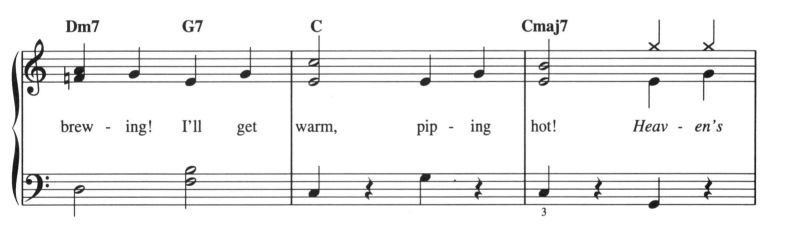

brew - ing! I'll get warm, pip - ing hot! *Heav - en's*

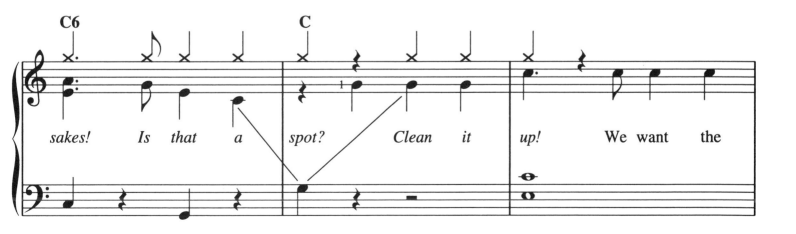

sakes! Is that a spot? Clean it up! We want the

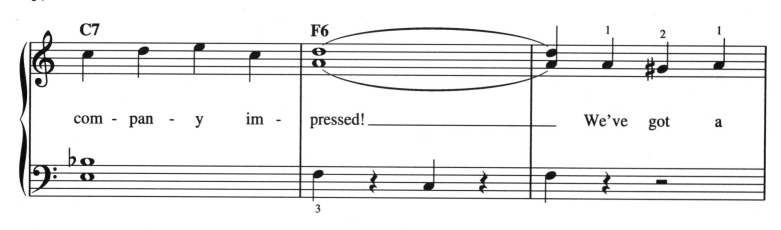

com - pan - y im - pressed! _____ We've got a

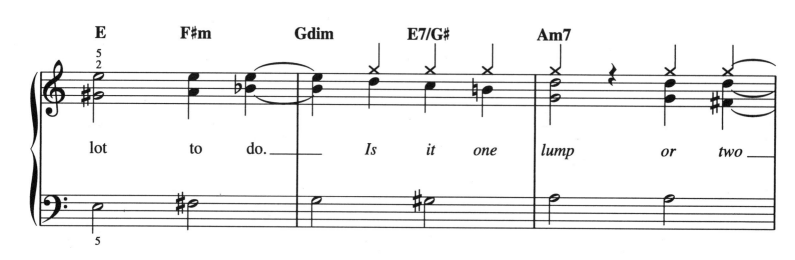

lot to do. ___ *Is it one lump or two* ___

___ *for you, our guest? Chorus:* She's our guest! *Mrs. Potts:* She's our

guest! *Chorus:* She's our guest! Be our guest! Be our

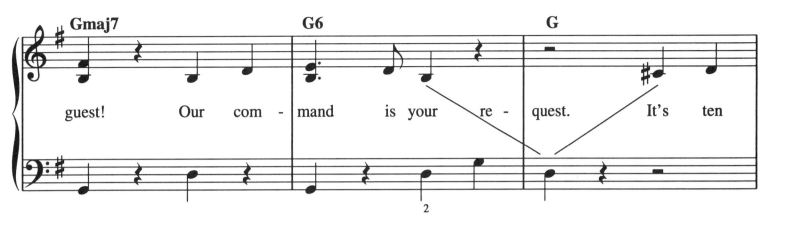

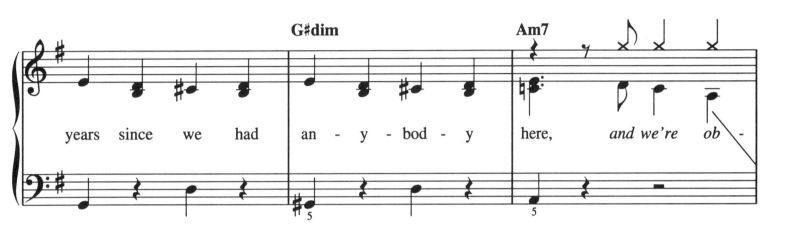

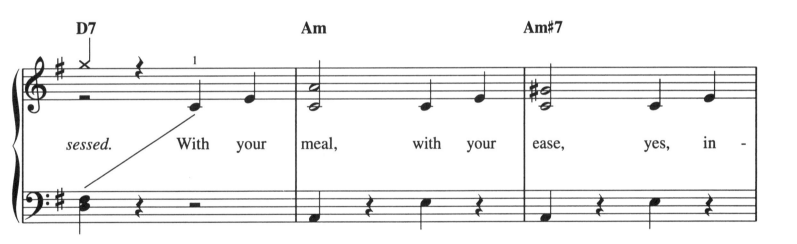

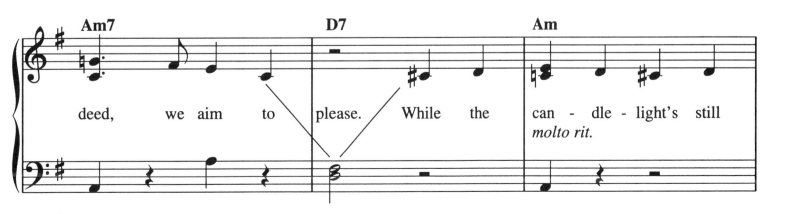

glow - ing let us help you, we'll keep go - ing course by

rit.

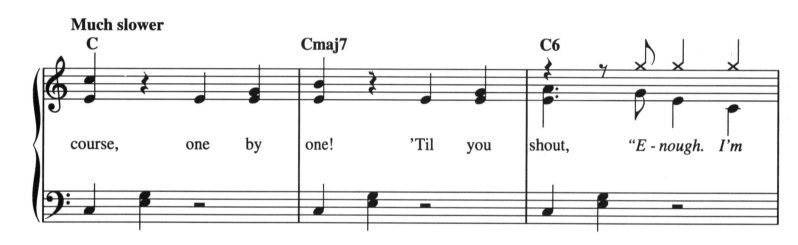

Much slower

course, one by one! 'Til you shout, "E - nough. I'm

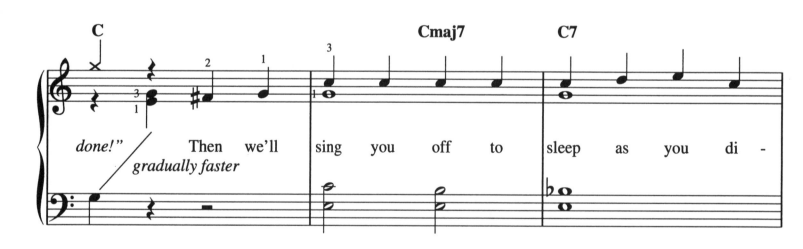

done!" Then we'll sing you off to sleep as you di -

gradually faster

gest. To - night you'll prop your feet

a tempo

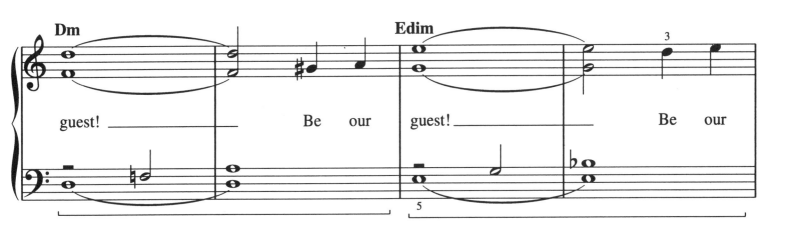

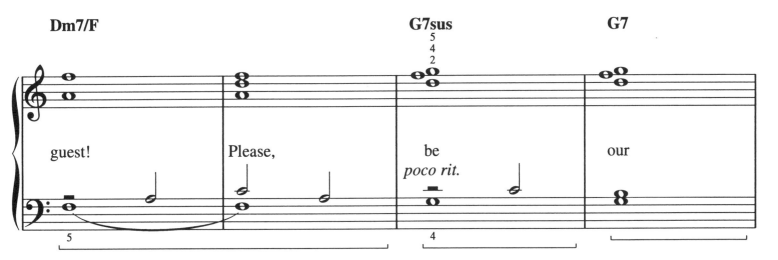

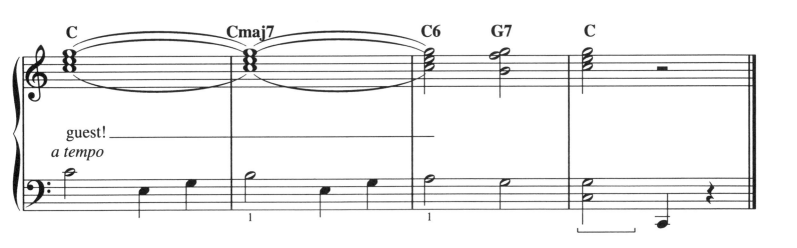

BEAUTY AND THE BEAST
from Walt Disney's BEAUTY AND THE BEAST

Lyrics by HOWARD ASHMAN
Music by ALAN MENKEN

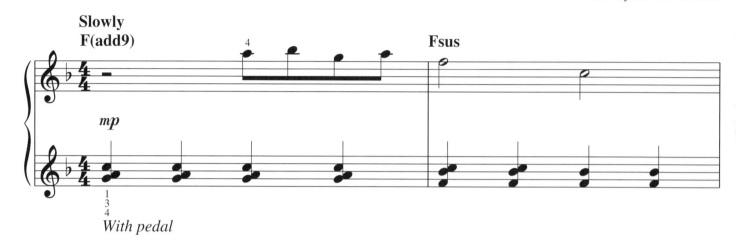

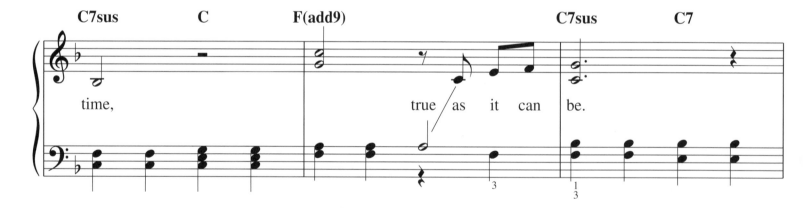

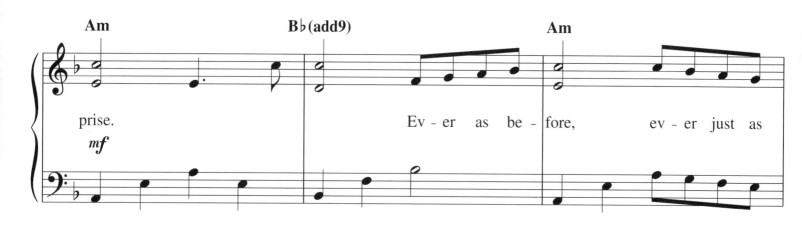

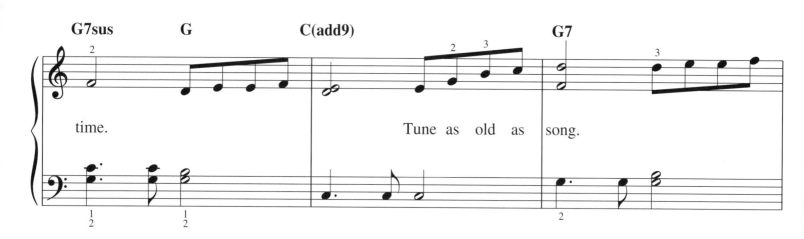

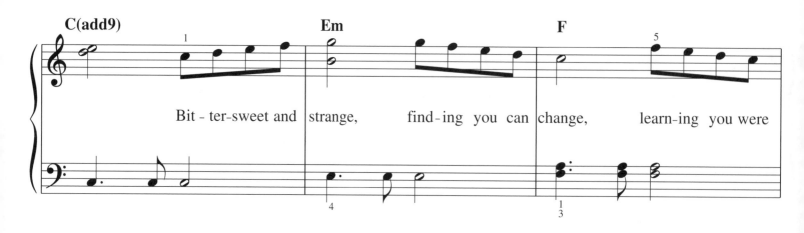

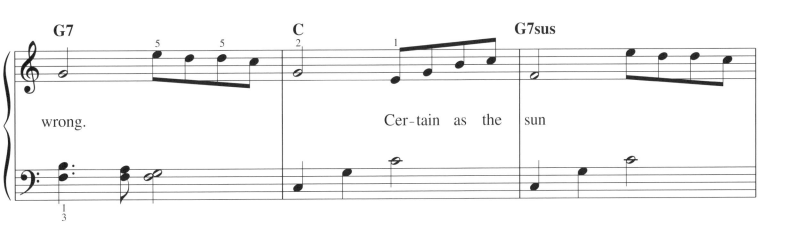

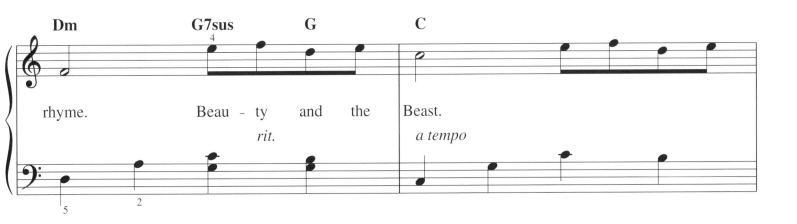

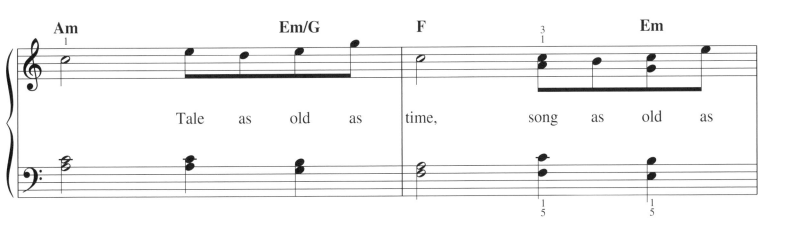

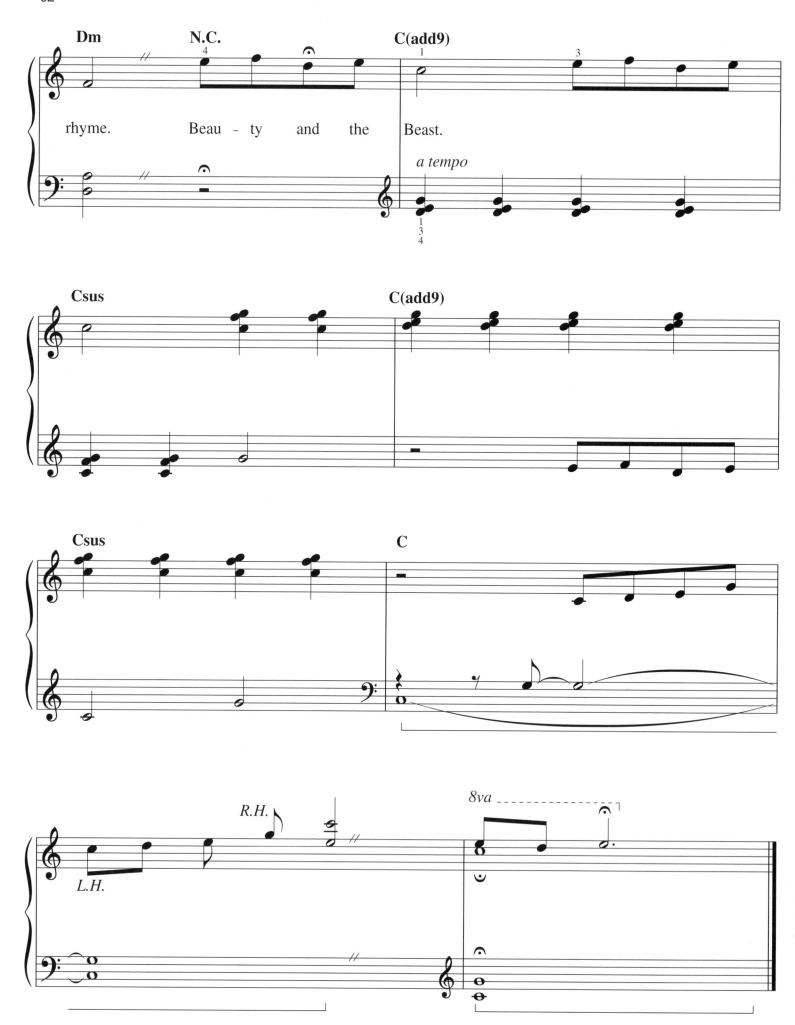

rhyme.   Beau – ty   and   the   Beast.

BELLE
from Walt Disney's BEAUTY AND THE BEAST

Lyrics by HOWARD ASHMAN
Music by ALAN MENKEN

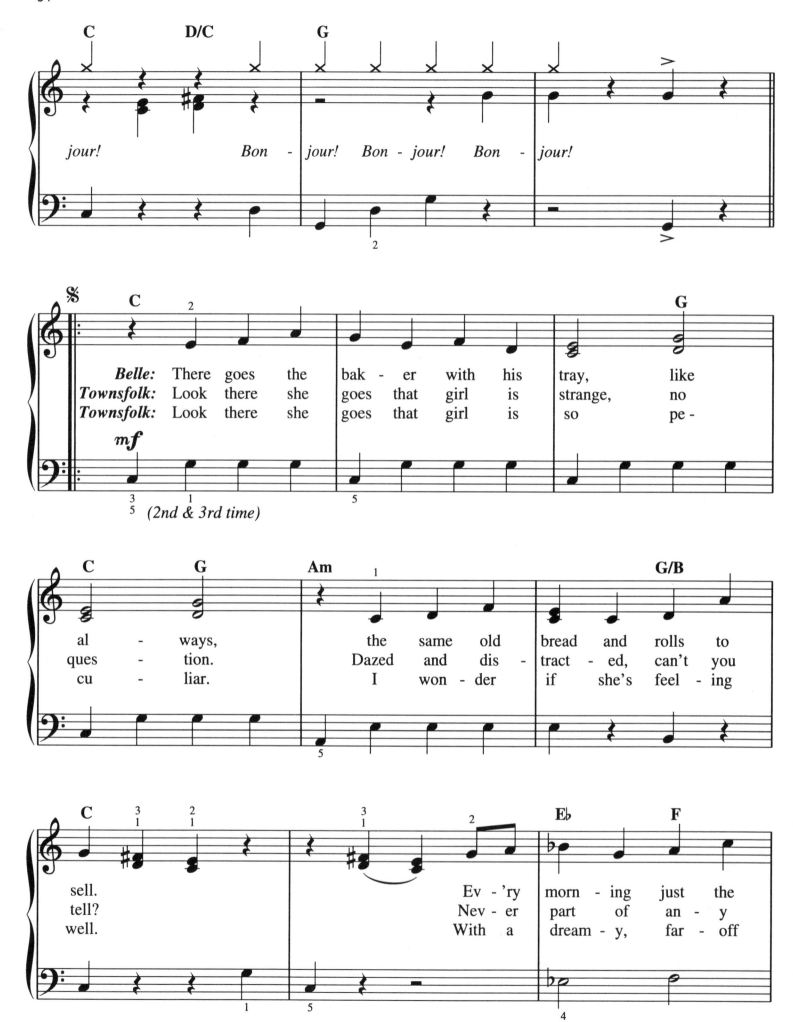

jour! Bon - jour! Bon - jour! Bon - jour!

Belle: There goes the bak - er with his tray, like
Townsfolk: Look there she goes that girl is strange, no
Townsfolk: Look there she goes that girl is so pe -

(2nd & 3rd time)

al - ways, the same old bread and rolls to
ques - tion. Dazed and dis - tract - ed, can't you
cu - liar. I won - der if she's feel - ing

sell. Ev - 'ry morn - ing just the
tell? Nev - er part of an - y
well. With a dream - y, far - off

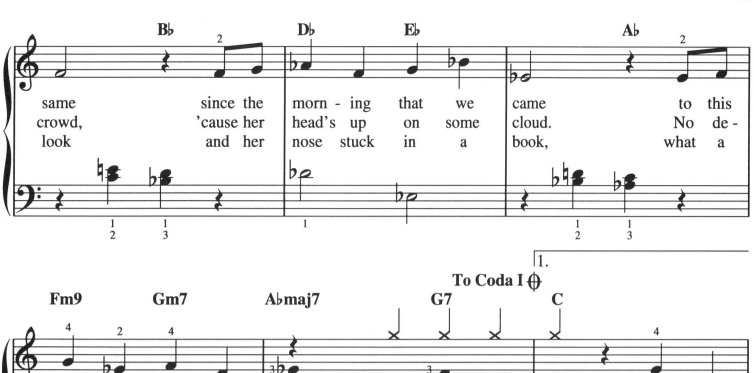

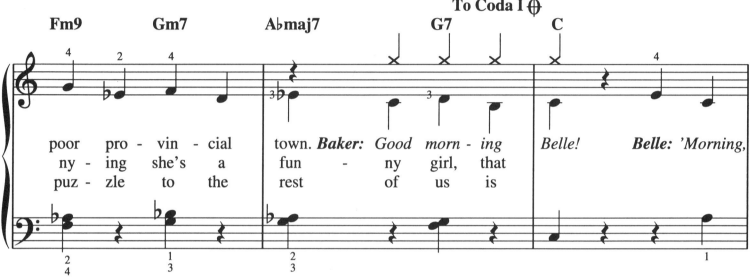

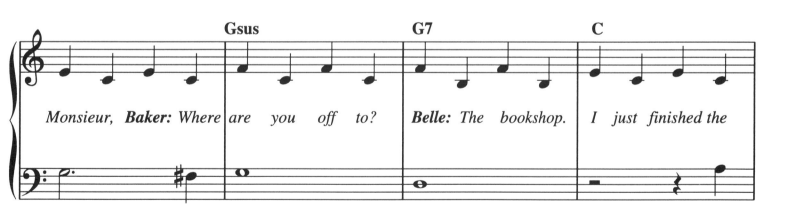

66

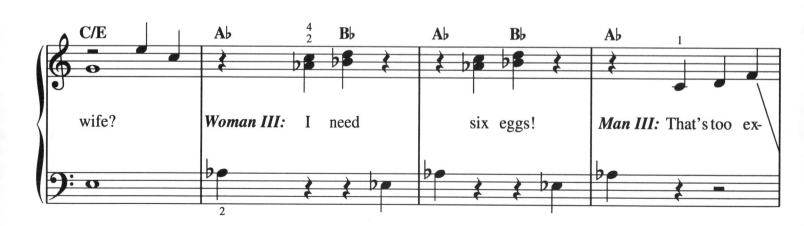

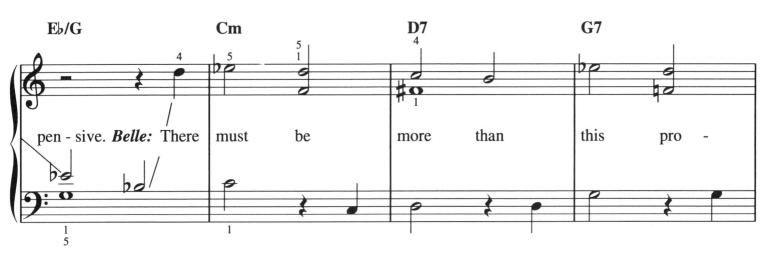

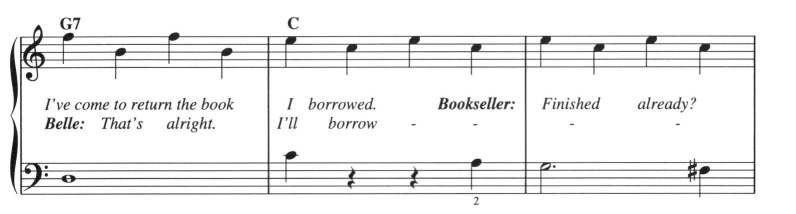

B♭sus | **B♭7** | **B♭sus** | **B♭7**

1.

favorite! | far off places, | 2. spells, a prince | in disguise...*Bookseller:*

C | | | 1. **Gsus**

If you like it all that | much, it's | yours! ***Belle:*** But
insist. ***Belle:*** Well, | thank you.

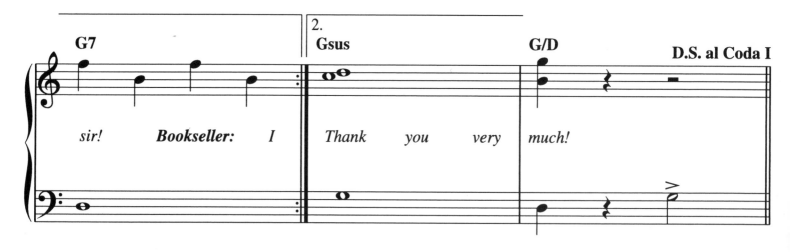

G7 | 2. **Gsus** | **G/D** | **D.S. al Coda I**

sir! ***Bookseller:*** I | Thank you very | much!

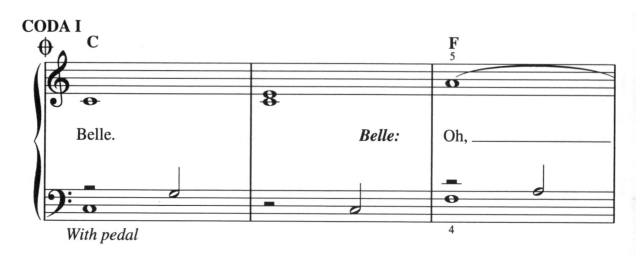

CODA I

C | | **F**

Belle. | | ***Belle:*** Oh, _____

With pedal

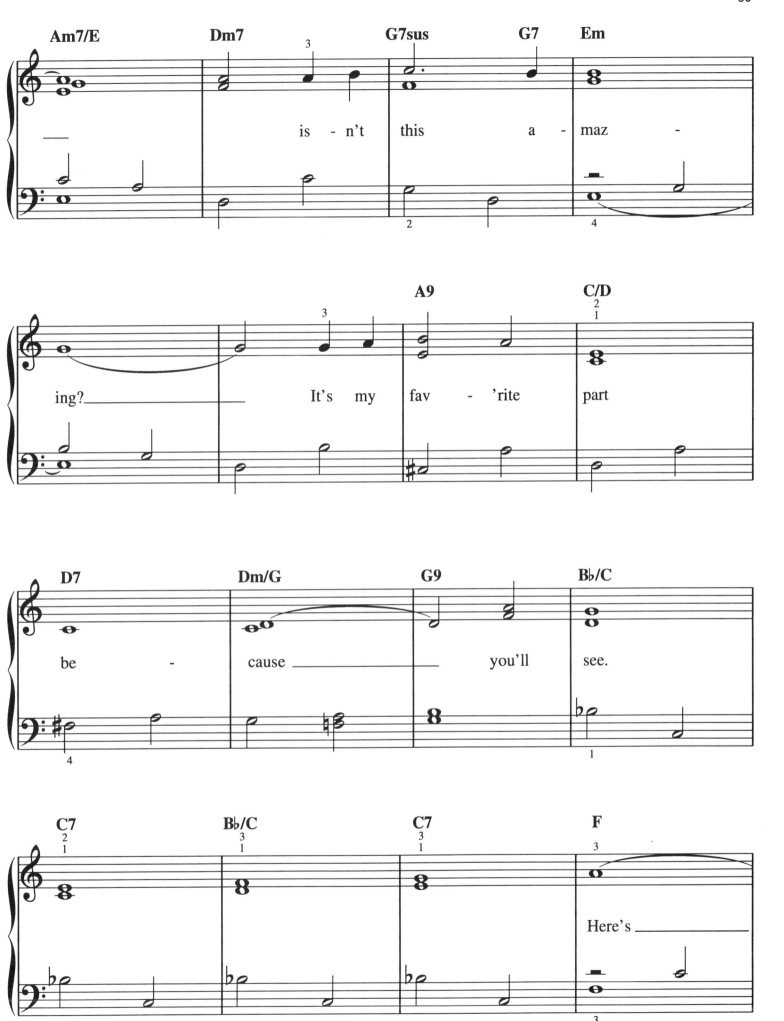

70

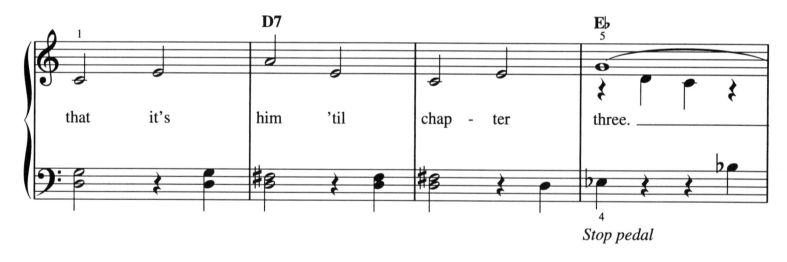

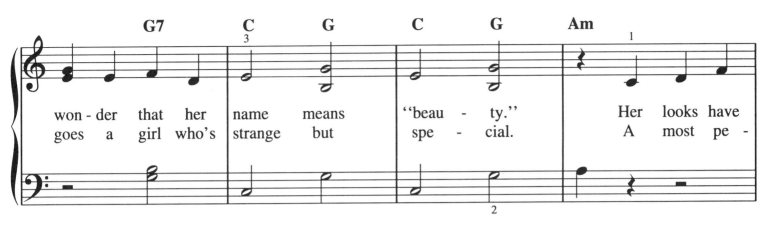

won - der that her name means "beau - ty." Her looks have
goes a girl who's strange but spe - cial. A most pe -

got no par - al - lel. *Shopkeeper:* But be- hind that fair fa -
cu - liar mad - 'moi - selle. It's a pit - y and a

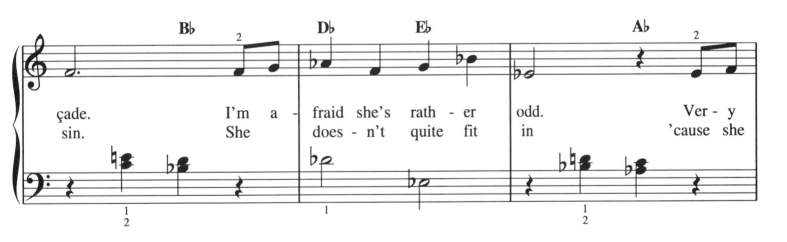

çade. I'm a - fraid she's rath - er odd. Ver - y
sin. She does - n't quite fit in 'cause she

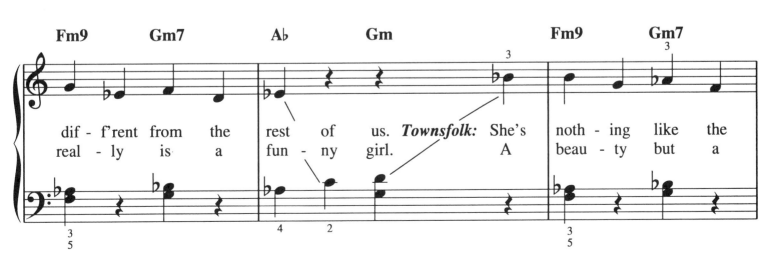

dif - f'rent from the rest of us. *Townsfolk:* She's noth - ing like the
real - ly is a fun - ny girl. A beau - ty but a

72

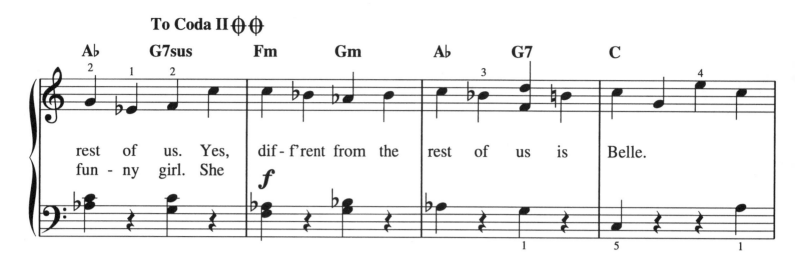

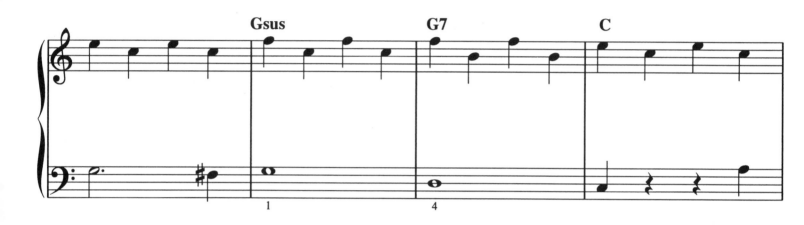

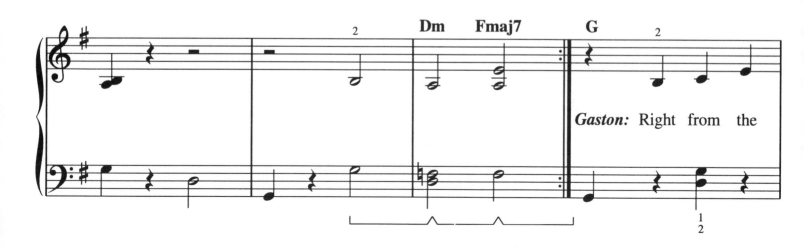

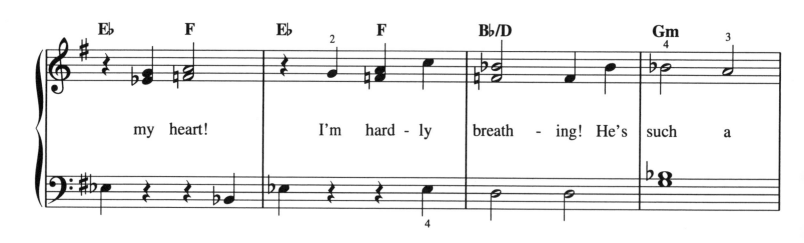

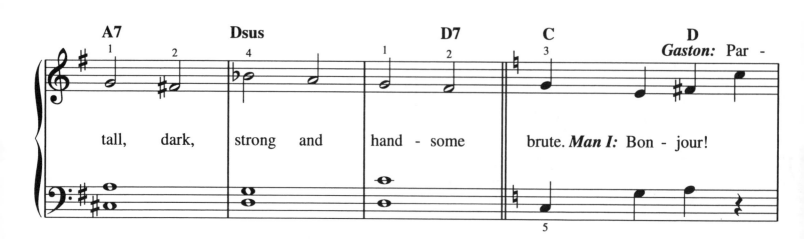

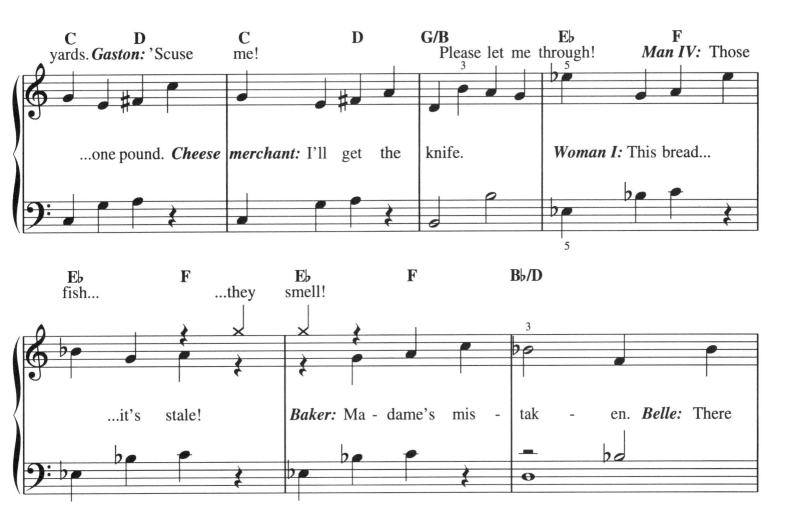

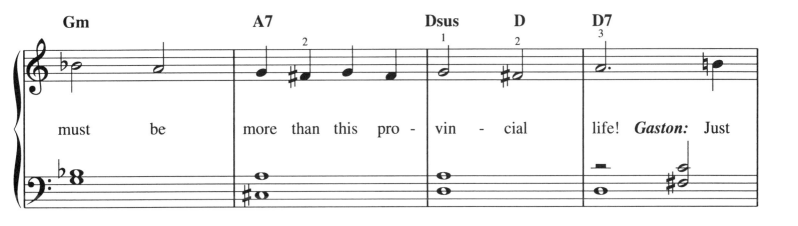

76

watch I'm go - ing to make Belle my wife!

real - ly is a fun - ny girl

that Belle!

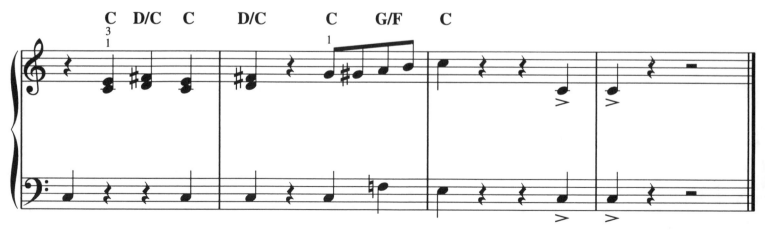

SOMETHING THERE
from Walt Disney's BEAUTY AND THE BEAST

Lyrics by HOWARD ASHMAN
Music by ALAN MENKEN

Beast: She glanced this fore.

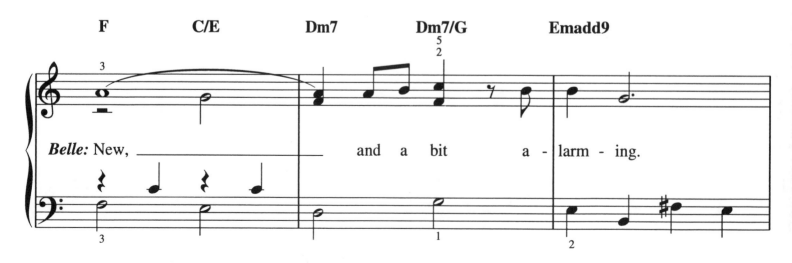

Belle: New, _____ and a bit a - larm - ing.

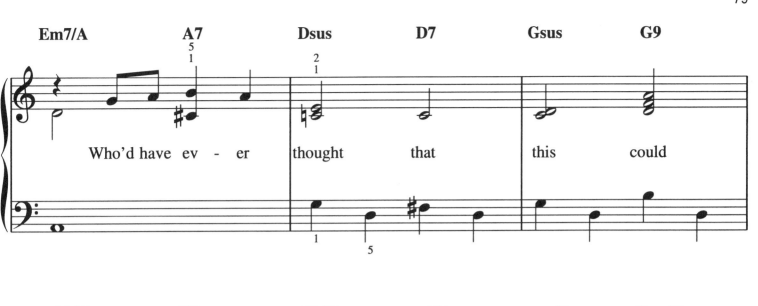

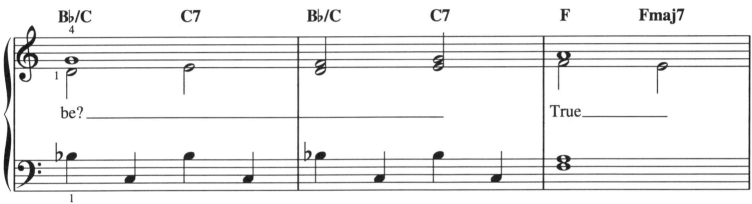

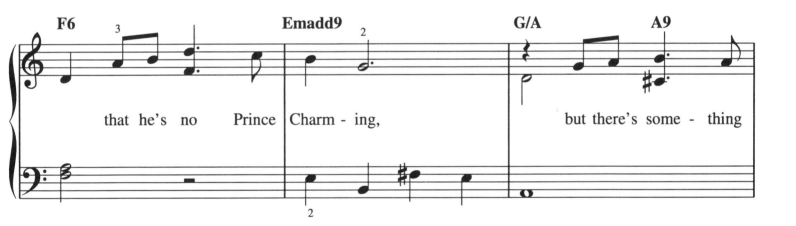

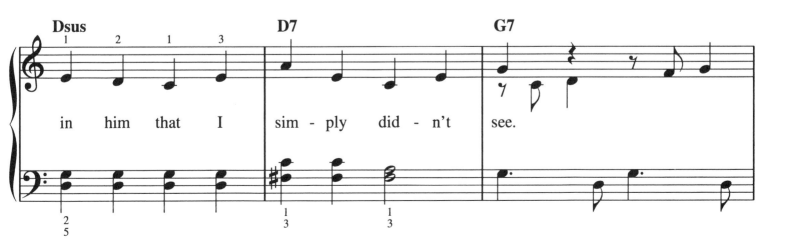

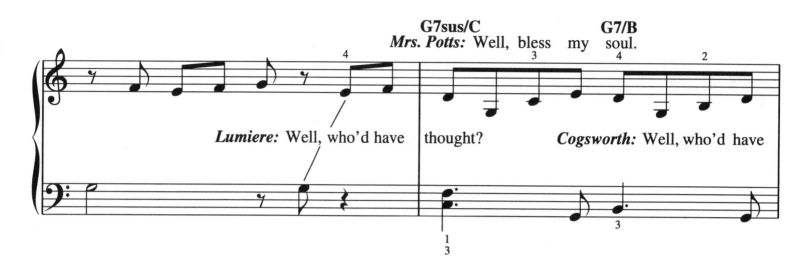

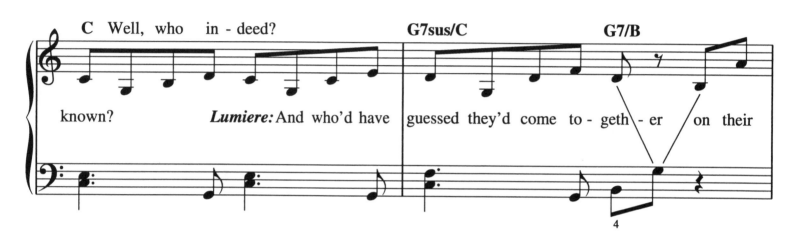

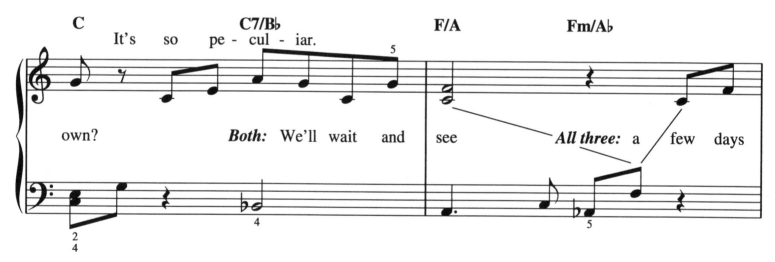

Cadd9   **C**   **G7sus**   **G7/B**

fore. *Cogsworth:* You know, perhaps there's something there that was-n't there be-

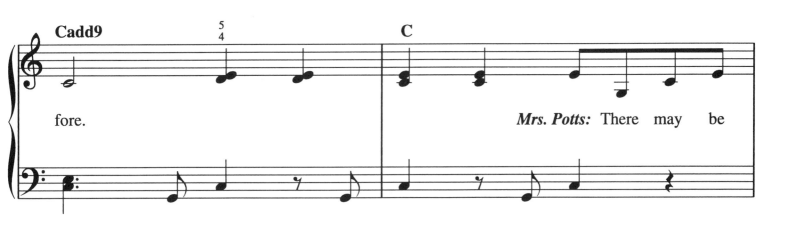

Cadd9   **C**

fore.   *Mrs. Potts:* There may be

G7sus   **G7/B**   **Cadd9**

some-thing there that was-n't there be- fore.

rit.

MY FUNNY FRIEND AND ME

from Walt Disney Pictures' THE EMPEROR'S NEW GROOVE

Lyrics by STING
Music by STING and DAVID HARTLEY

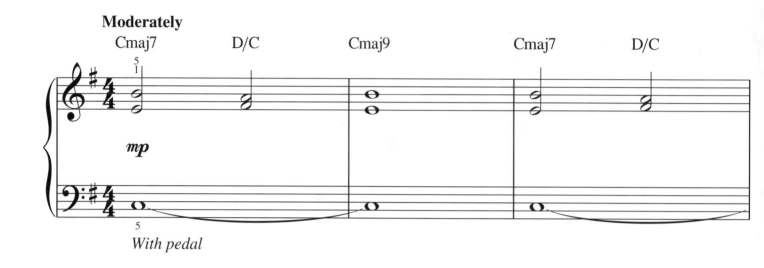

In the qui - et time of eve - ning,
that the world is not my play - ground;

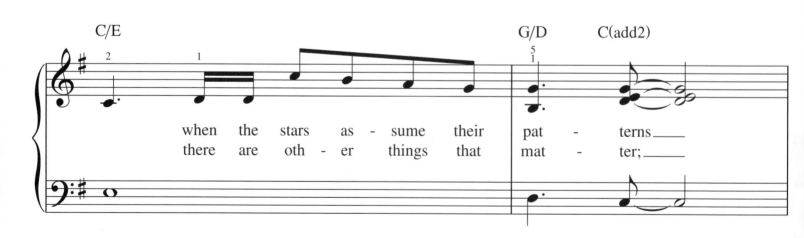

when the stars as - sume their pat - terns_____
there are oth - er things that mat - ter;_____

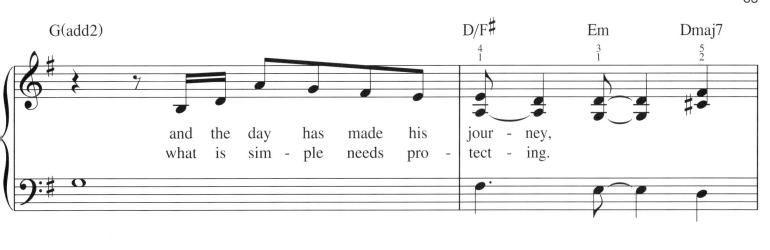

G(add2)   D/F#   Em   Dmaj7

and the day has made his jour - ney,
what is sim - ple needs pro - tect - ing.

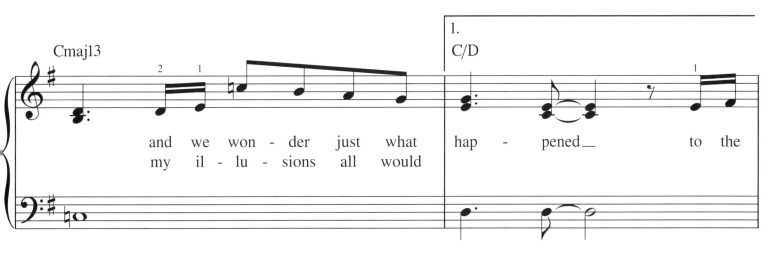

Cmaj13   1.
                                    C/D

and we won - der just what hap - pened___ to the
my il - lu - sions all would

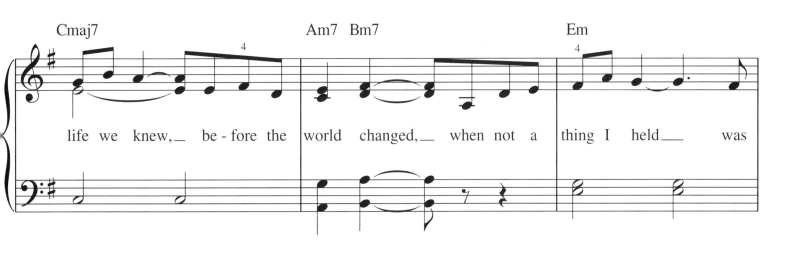

Cmaj7   Am7 Bm7   Em

life we knew,___ be - fore the world changed,___ when not a thing I held___ was

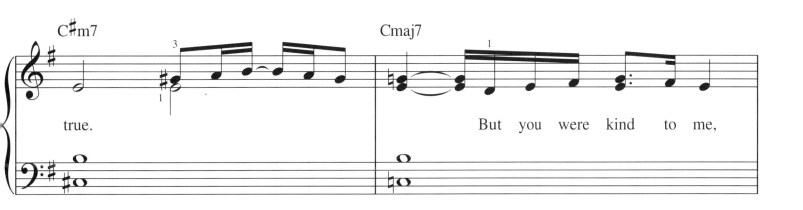

C#m7   Cmaj7

true.   But you were kind to me,

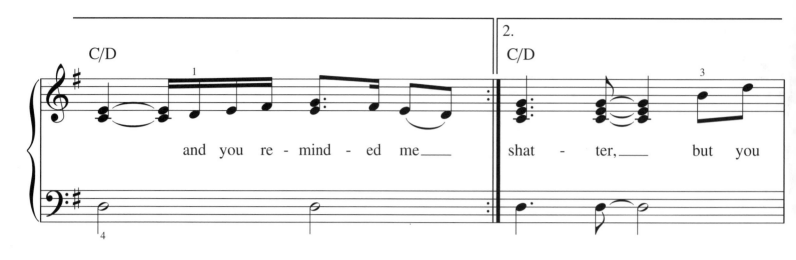

and you re - mind - ed me___ shat - ter,___ but you

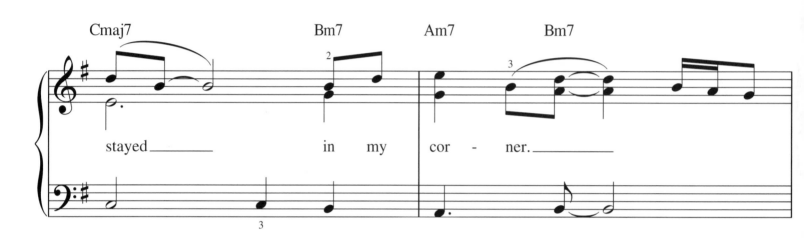

stayed_____ in my cor - ner._____

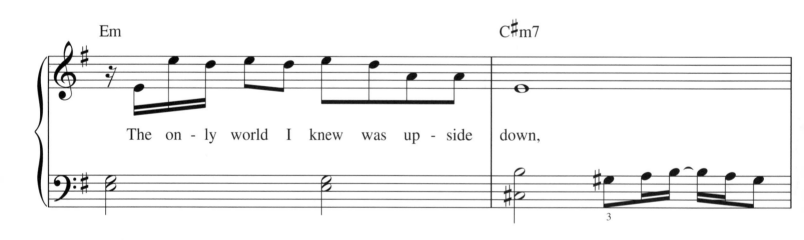

The on - ly world I knew was up - side down,

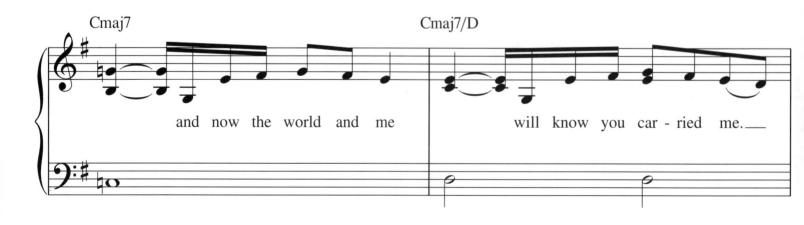

and now the world and me will know you car - ried me.___

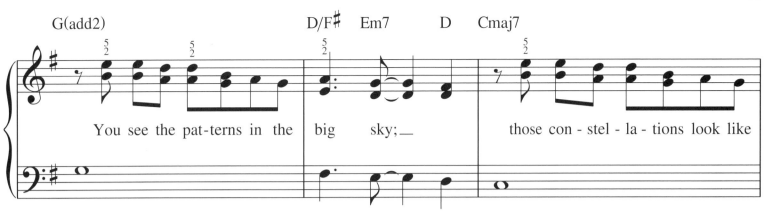

You see the pat-terns in the big sky; — those con - stel - la - tions look like

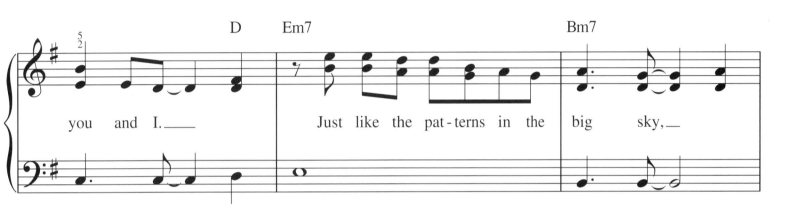

you and I. — Just like the pat-terns in the big sky, —

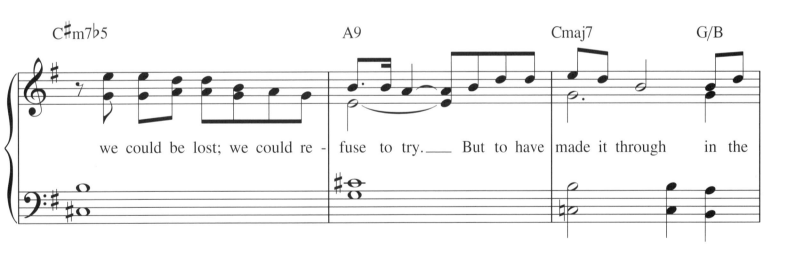

we could be lost; we could re - fuse to try. — But to have made it through in the

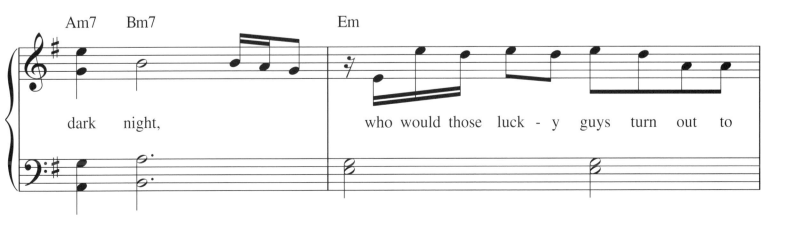

dark night, who would those luck - y guys turn out to

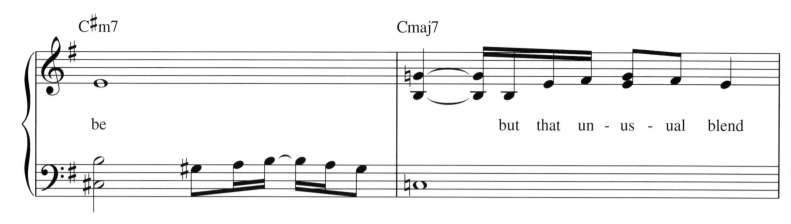

C#m7
be

Cmaj7
but that un - us - ual blend

Cmaj7/D
of my fun - ny friend and

G(add2)
me.

D/F#   Cmaj9

G(add2)
I'm not as clev - er as I

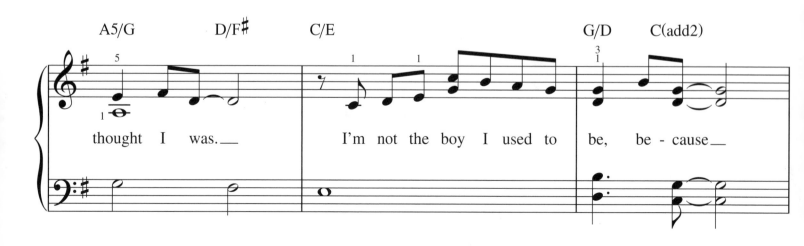

A5/G   D/F#   C/E
thought I was.___   I'm not the boy I used to

G/D   C(add2)
be, be - cause___

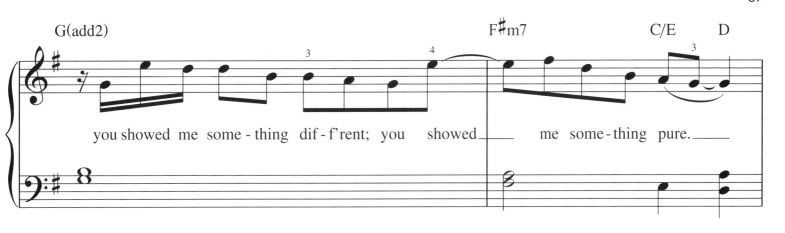

G(add2)   F♯m7   C/E   D

you showed me some-thing dif-f'rent; you showed___ me some-thing pure.___

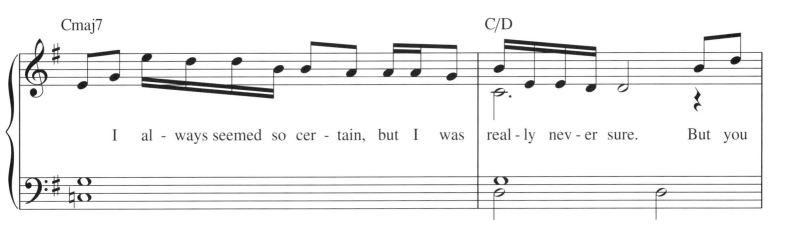

Cmaj7   C/D

I al-ways seemed so cer-tain, but I was real-ly nev-er sure. But you

Cmaj7   Am7   Bm7

stayed,_____ and you called my name___

Em   C♯m7

when oth-ers would have walked out on a lou-sy game.

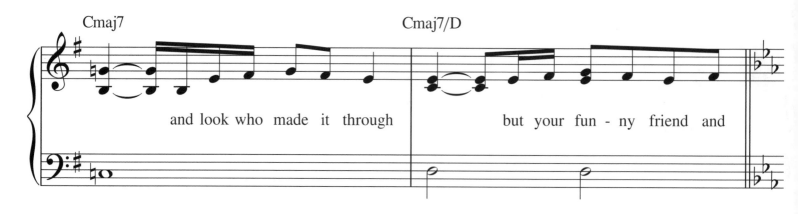

Cmaj7 | Cmaj7/D

and look who made it through | but your fun - ny friend and

Eb(add2) | Bb/D Ab/C | Bb6 Abmaj7

you. You see the pat-terns in the | big sky.__ | Those con - stel - la - tions look like

Bb Cm7 | Cm/Bb

you and I.__ | That ti - ny plan - et and the | big - ger guy.__

Abmaj7 | Bb7sus F(add2)

I don't know wheth-er I should laugh or cry. | Just like the pat-terns in the

C/E   B♭/D   C6   B♭maj7   B♭/C   C

big   sky,___   we'll be to - geth - er 'til the   end this   time.___

Dm7   Dm/C

Don't   know   the   an - swer   or   the   rea - son   why.___

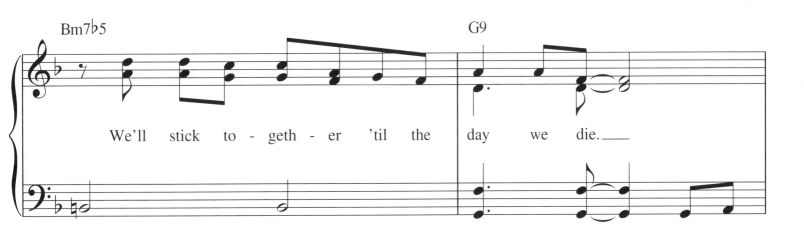

Bm7♭5   G9

We'll   stick   to - geth - er   'til   the   day   we   die.___

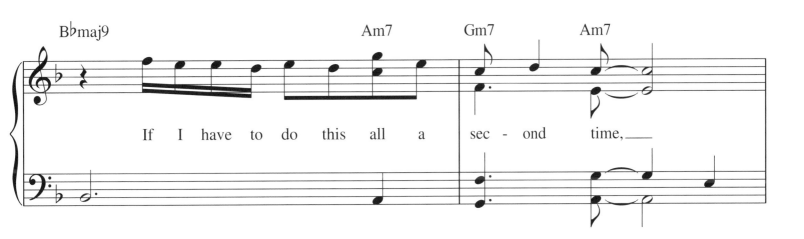

B♭maj9   Am7   Gm7   Am7

If   I   have   to   do   this   all   a   sec - ond   time,___

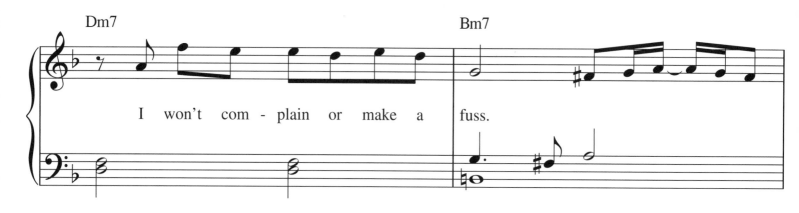

I won't com - plain or make a fuss.

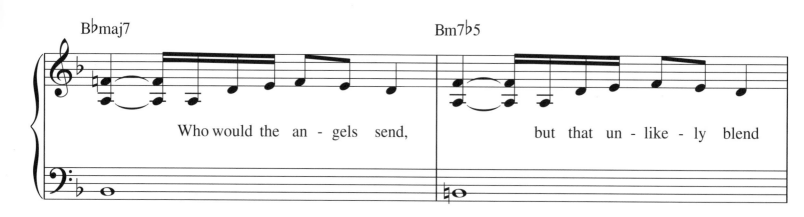

Who would the an - gels send,

but that un - like - ly blend

Slower

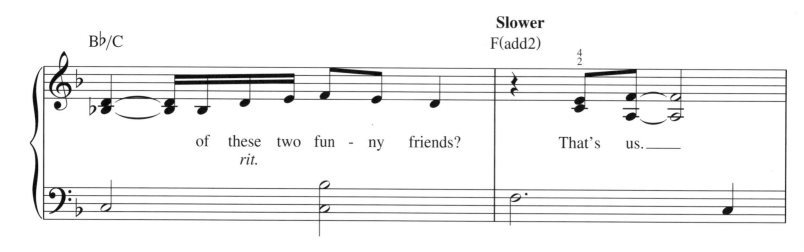

of these two fun - ny friends?
rit.

That's us.____

GO THE DISTANCE

from Walt Disney Pictures' HERCULES

Music by ALAN MENKEN
Lyrics by DAVID ZIPPEL

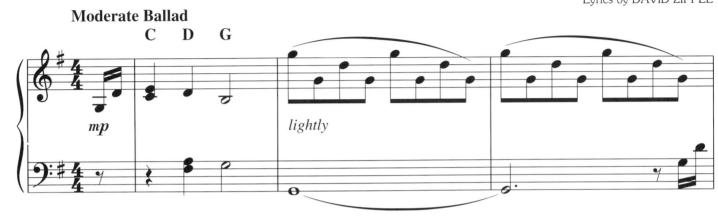

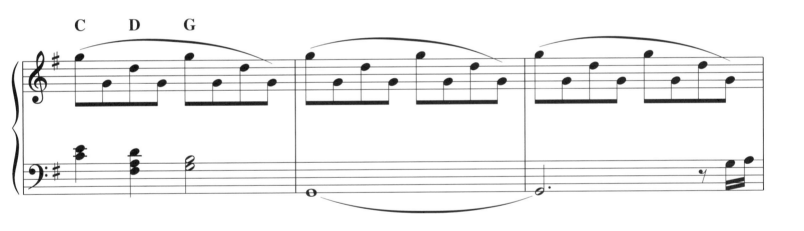

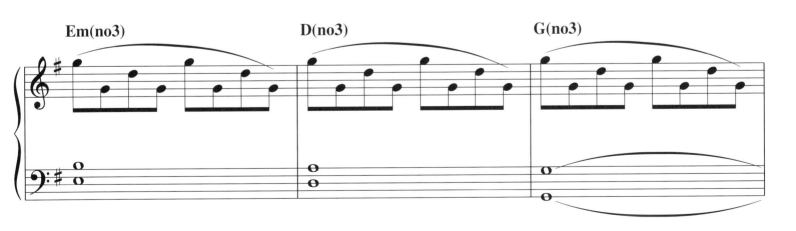

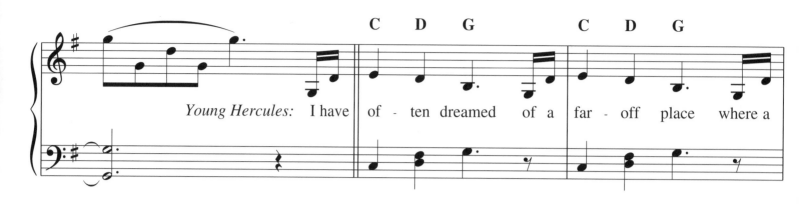

Young Hercules: I have of - ten dreamed of a far - off place where a

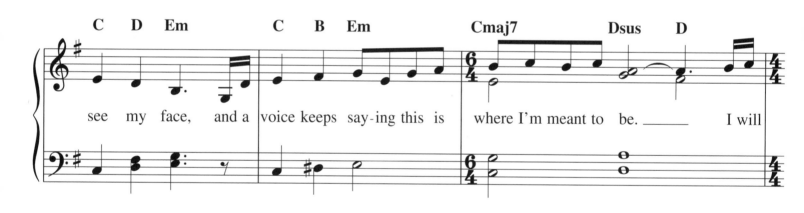

great warm wel-come will be wait - ing for me. Where the crowds will cheer when they

see my face, and a voice keeps say-ing this is where I'm meant to be. _____ I will

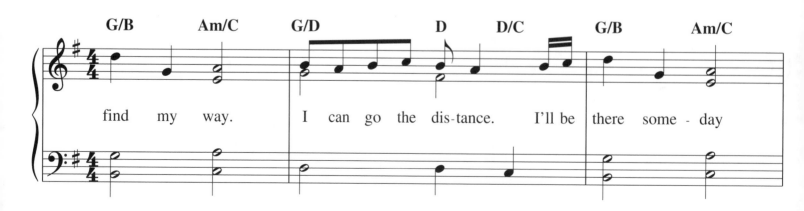

find my way. I can go the dis-tance. I'll be there some - day

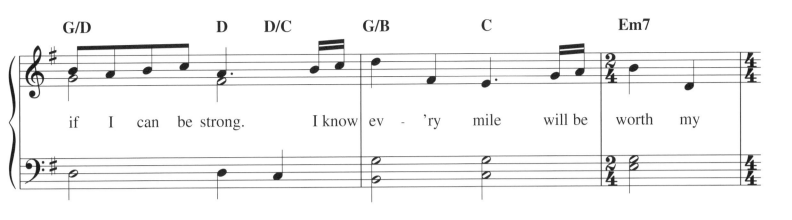

if I can be strong. I know ev - 'ry mile will be worth my

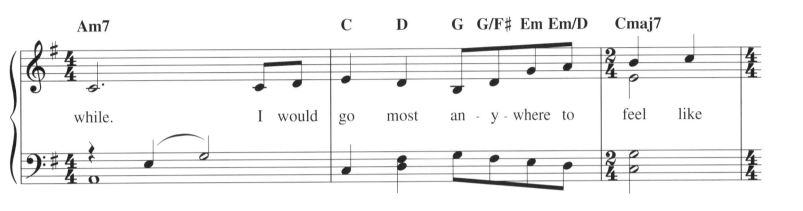

while. I would go most an - y - where to feel like

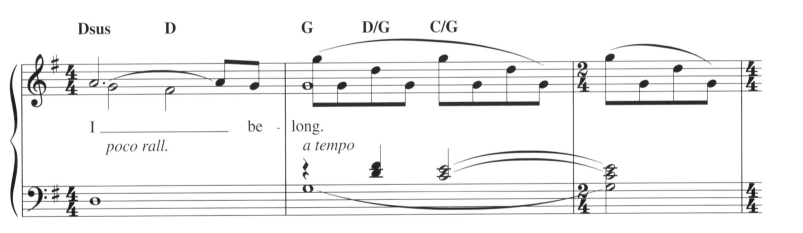

I _____ be - long.

poco rall.   *a tempo*

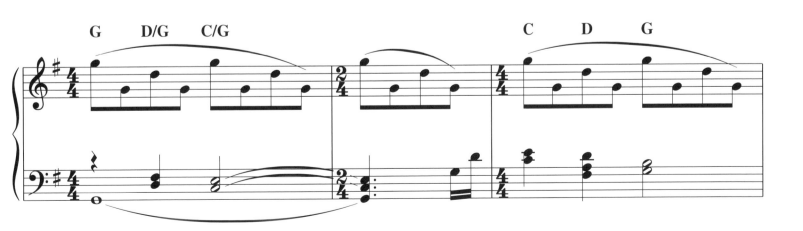

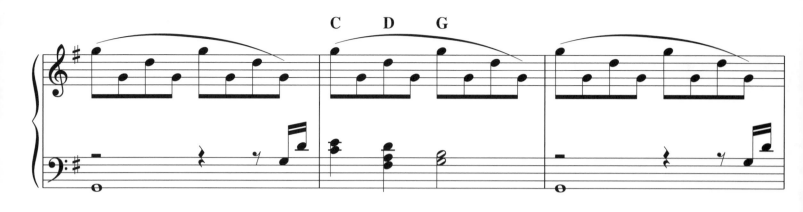

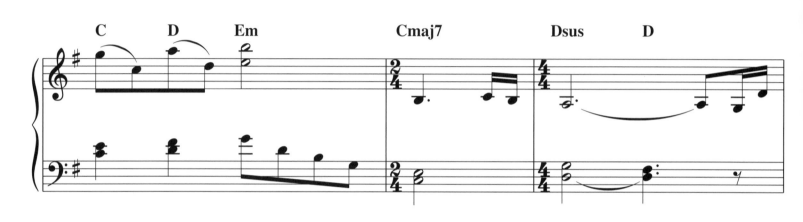

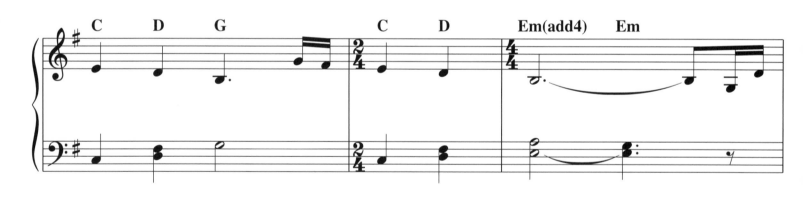

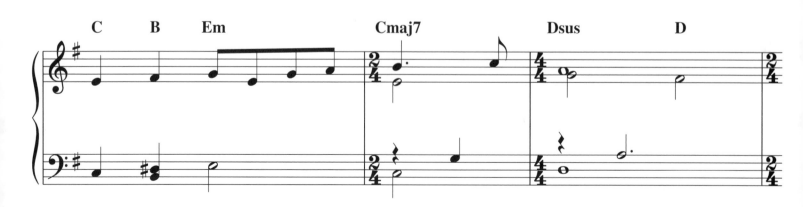

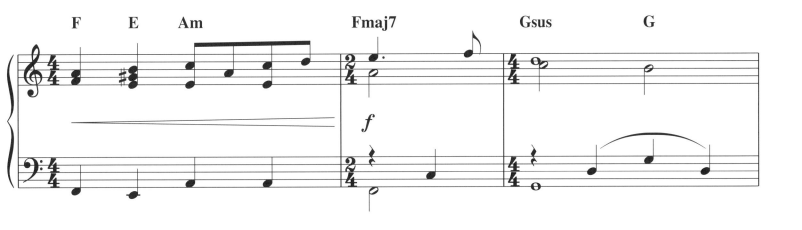

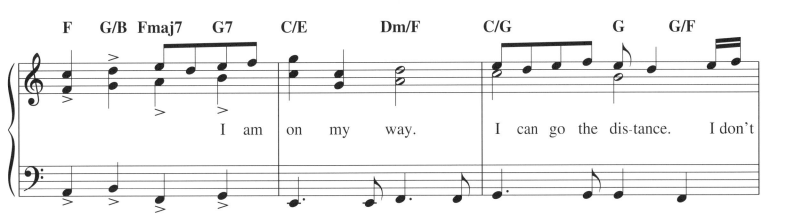

I am on my way. I can go the dis-tance. I don't

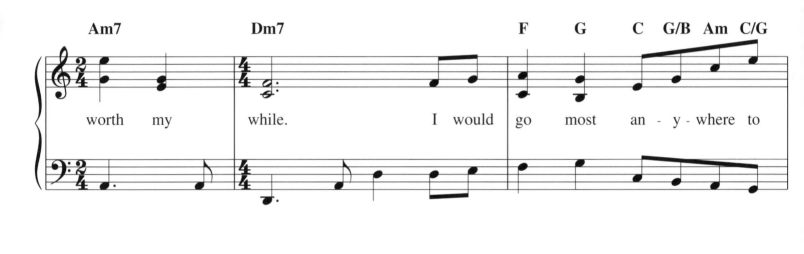

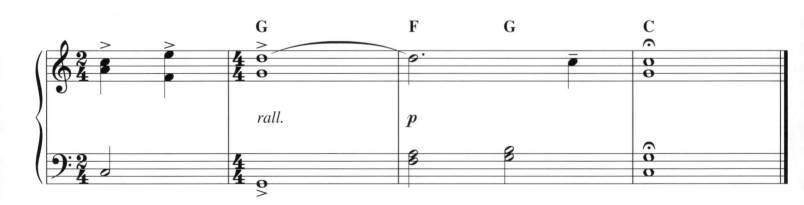

I WON'T SAY

(I'm in Love)
from Walt Disney Pictures' HERCULES

Music by ALAN MENKEN
Lyrics by DAVID ZIPPEL

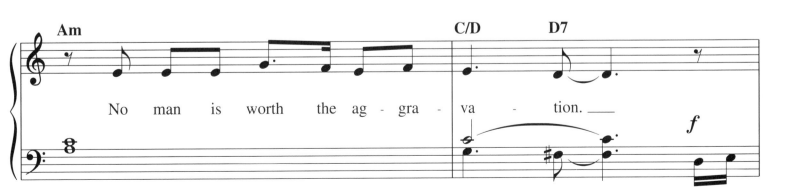

Moderate Rock

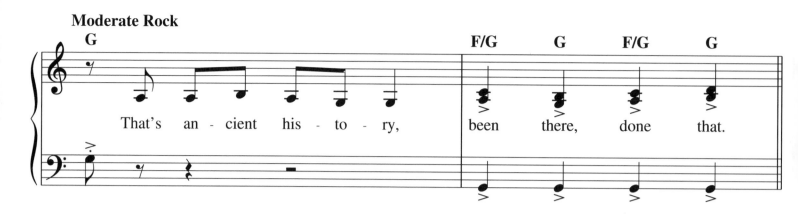

That's an - cient his - to - ry, been there, done that.

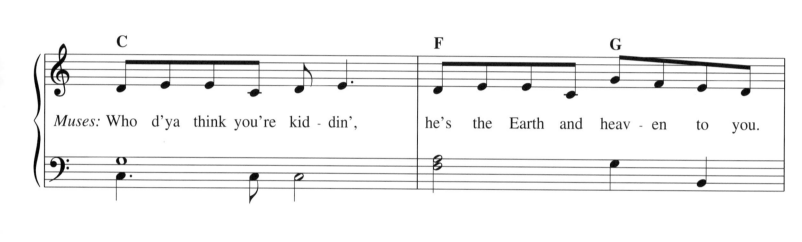

Muses: Who d'ya think you're kid - din', he's the Earth and heav - en to you.

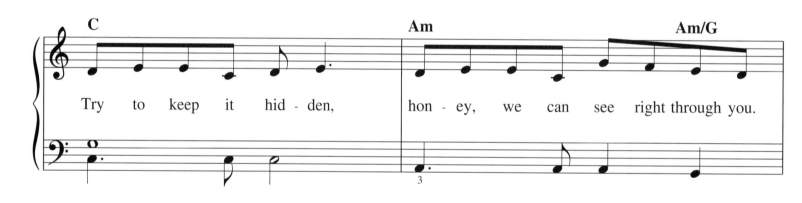

Try to keep it hid - den, hon - ey, we can see right through you.

Girl, ya can't con - ceal it, we know how ya feel and who you're

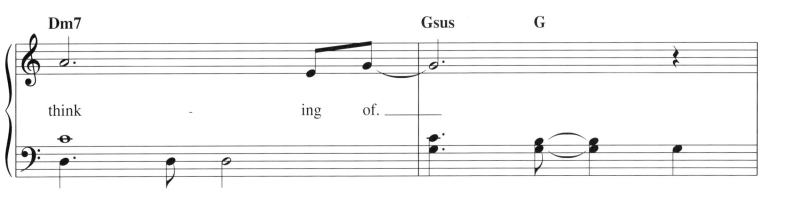

think - - ing of.

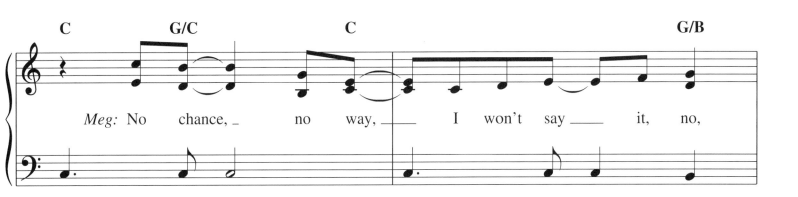

Meg: No chance, _ no way, _ I won't say _ it, no,

no. *Muses:* You swoon, _ you sigh, _ why de - ny _ it, uh

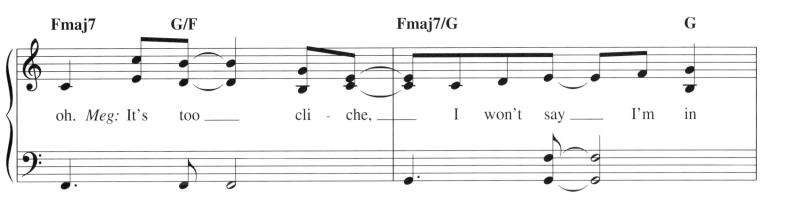

oh. *Meg:* It's too _ cli - che, _ I won't say _ I'm in

love.

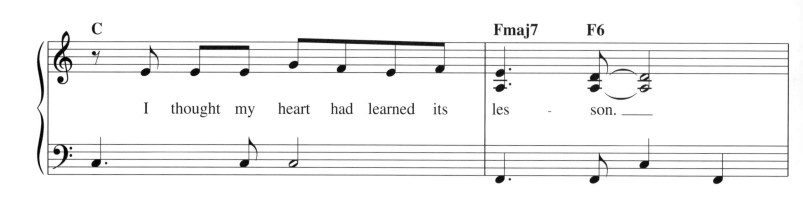

I thought my heart had learned its les - son. ___

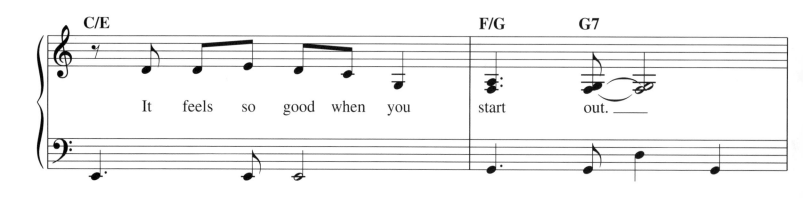

It feels so good when you start out. ___

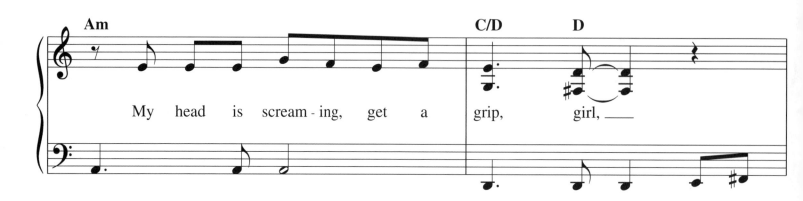

My head is scream - ing, get a grip, girl, ___

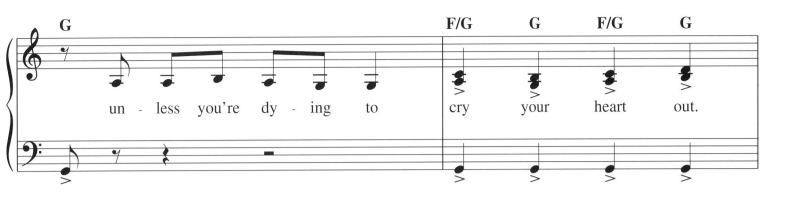

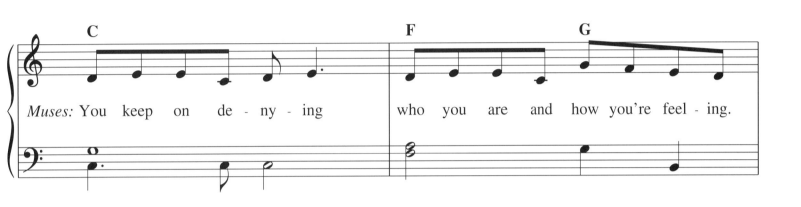

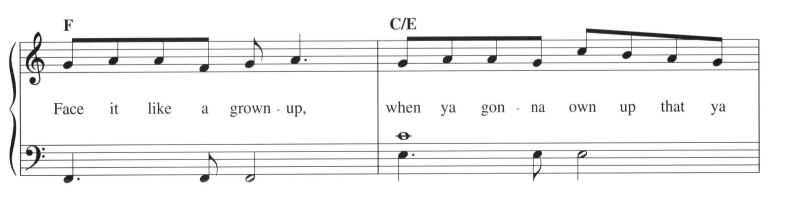

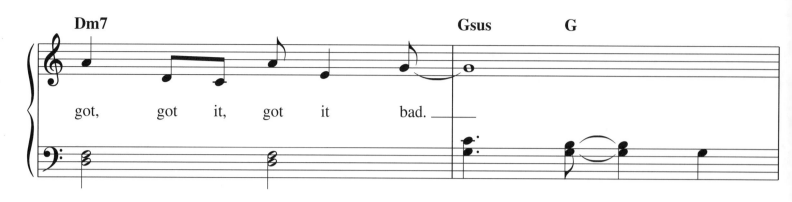

got, got it, got it bad.

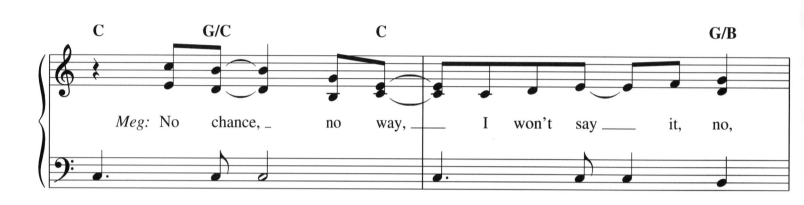

Meg: No chance, _ no way, ___ I won't say ___ it, no,

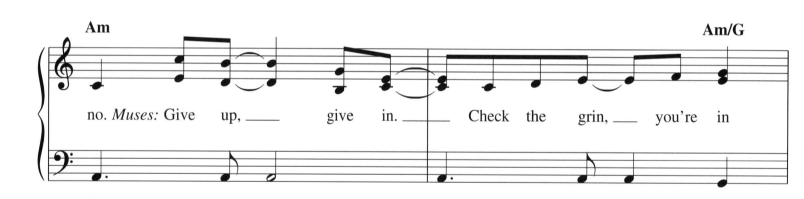

no. *Muses:* Give up, ___ give in. ___ Check the grin, ___ you're in

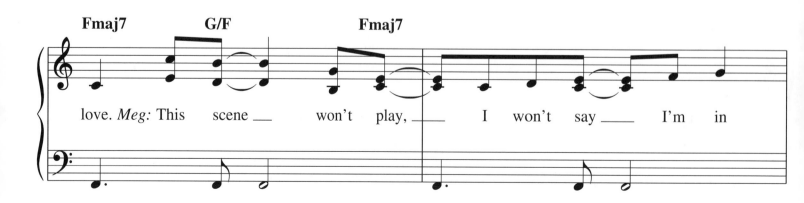

love. *Meg:* This scene ___ won't play, ___ I won't say ___ I'm in

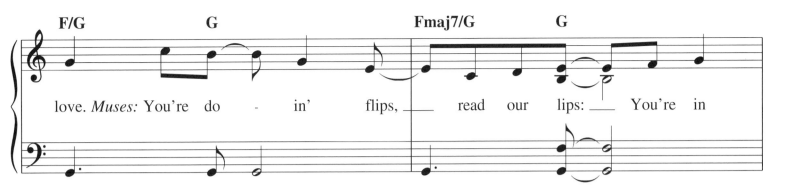

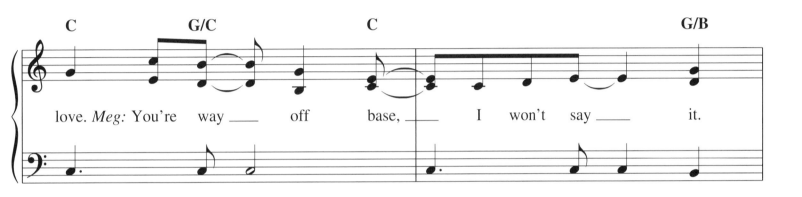

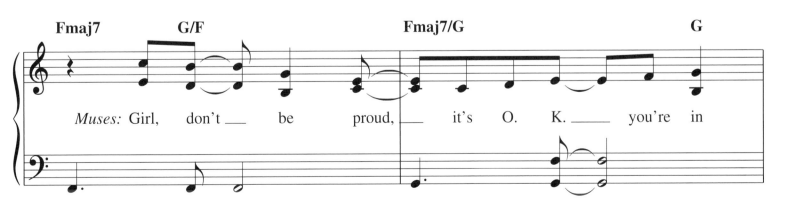

104

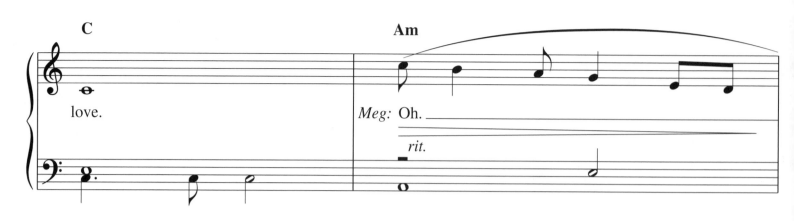

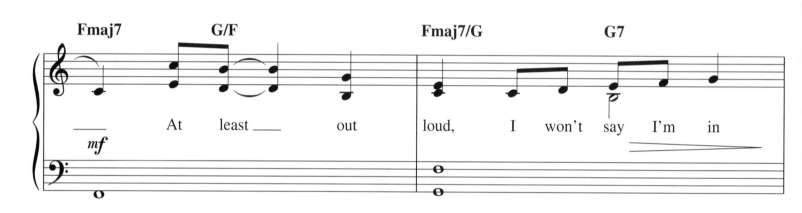

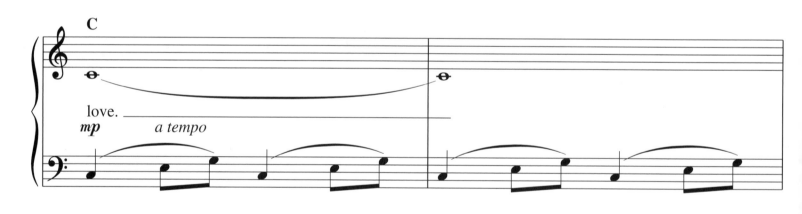

ONE LAST HOPE

from Walt Disney Pictures' HERCULES

Music by ALAN MENKEN
Lyrics by DAVID ZIPPEL

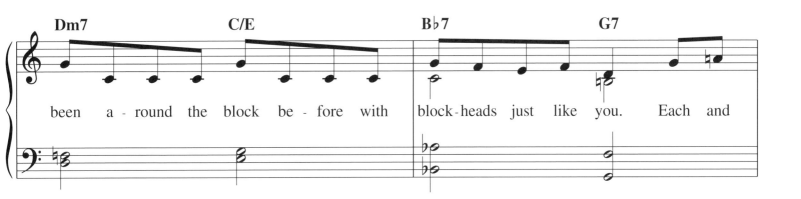

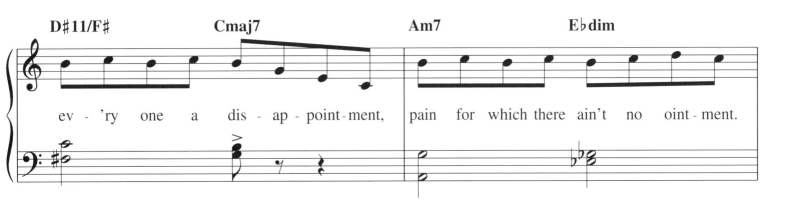

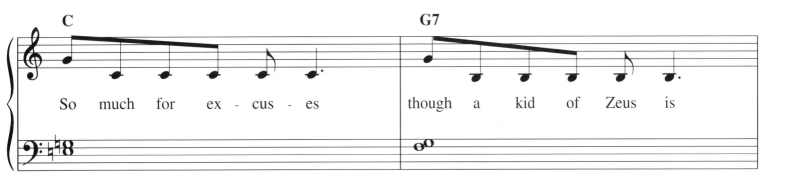

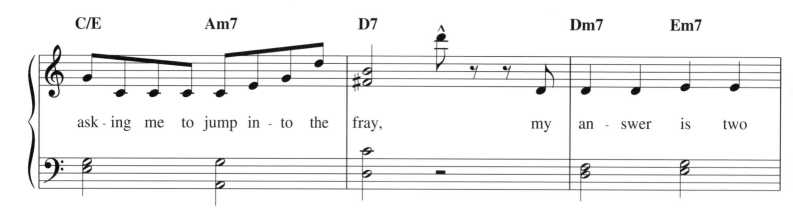

ask - ing me to jump in - to the fray, my an - swer is two

Moderate slow tempo

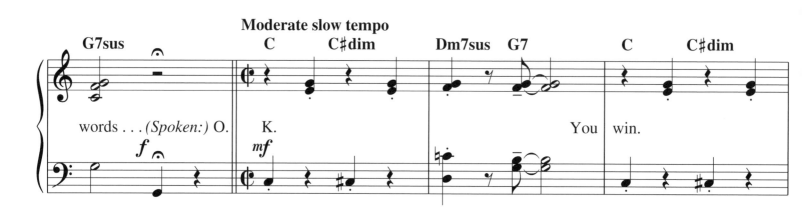

words . . . *(Spoken:)* O. K. You win.

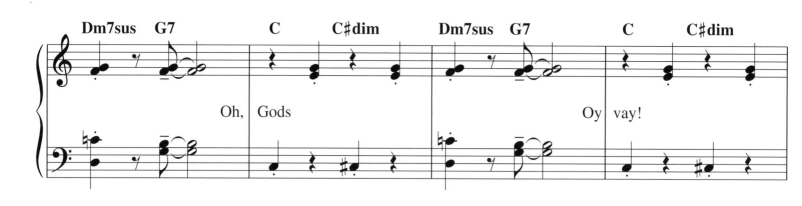

Oh, Gods Oy vay!

(Sung:) I'd giv - en up hope that some - one would

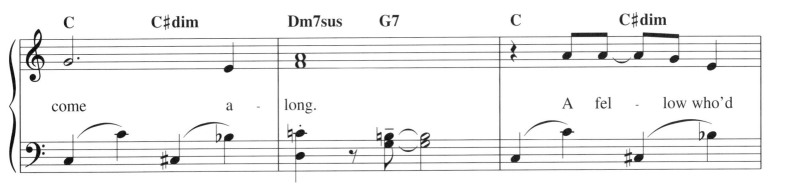

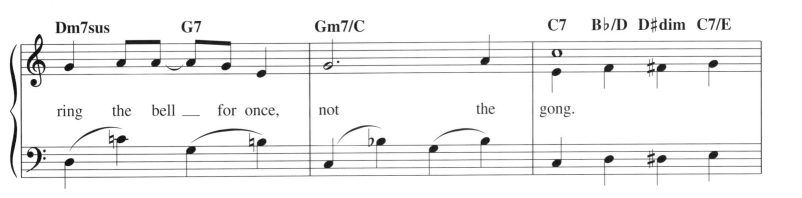

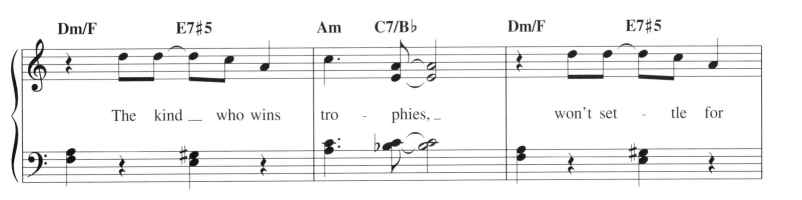

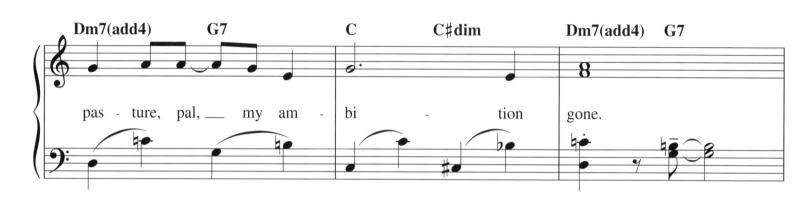

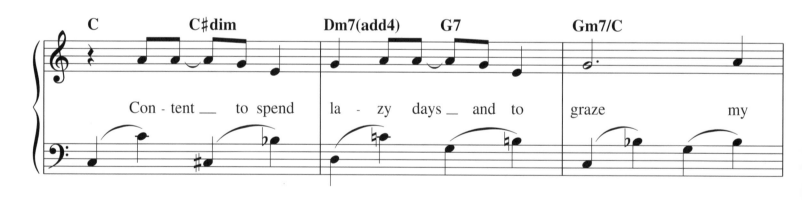

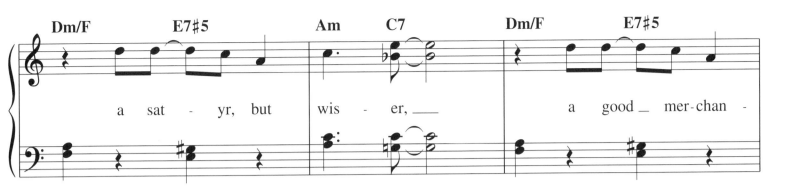

a sat - yr, but wis - er, ___ a good ___ mer-chan -

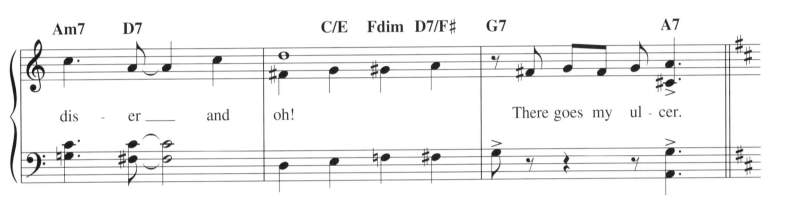

dis - er ___ and oh! There goes my ul - cer.

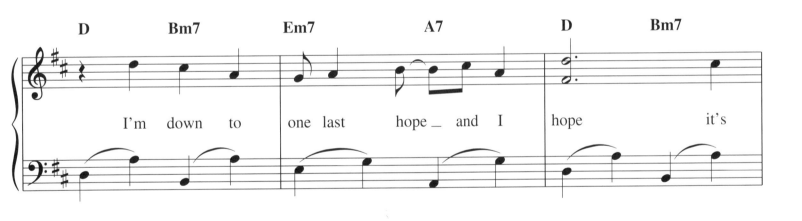

I'm down to one last hope ___ and I hope it's

you. Though, kid, you're not ex - act - ly a

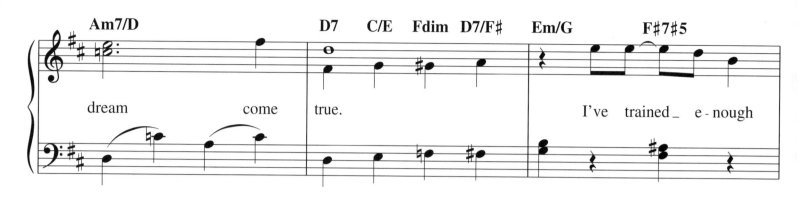

dream come true.

I've trained _ e - nough

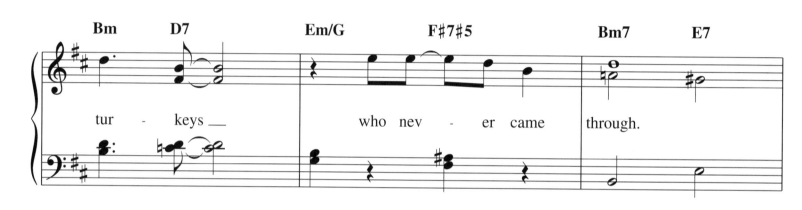

tur - keys __

who nev - er came through.

You're my one last hope so you'll have to do.

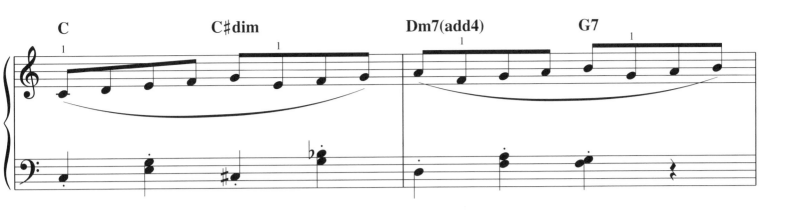

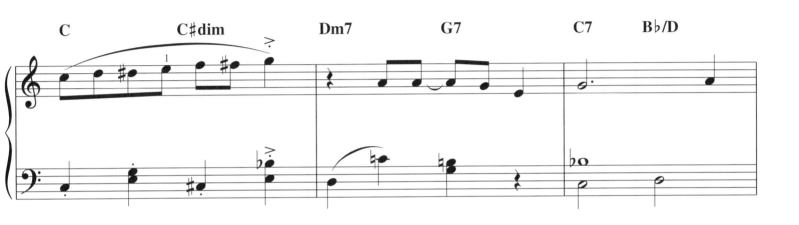

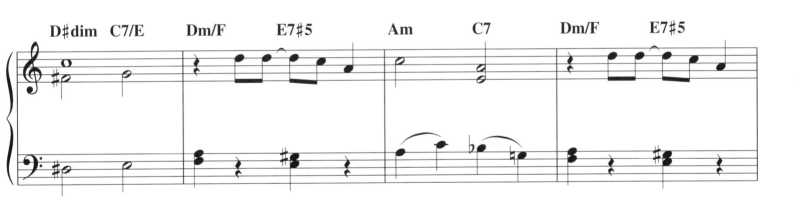

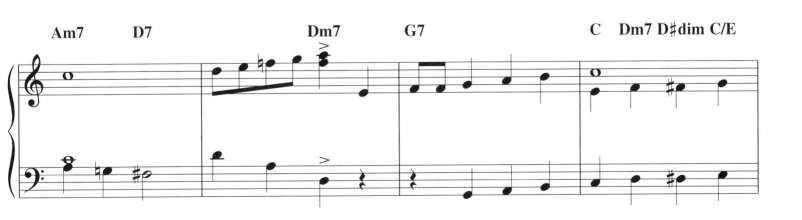

Dem - i Gods _ have faced the odds _ and

end - ed up in mock - er - y. ____ Don't be - lieve _ the

sto - ries that __ you read on all the crock - er - y. ____

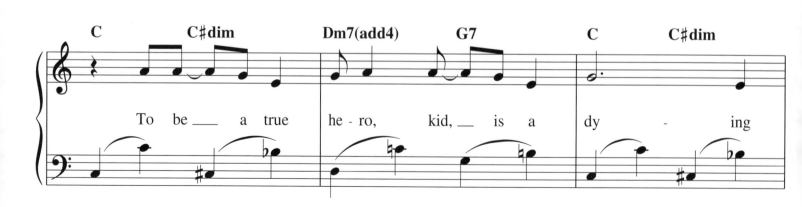

To be __ a true he - ro, kid, __ is a dy - ing

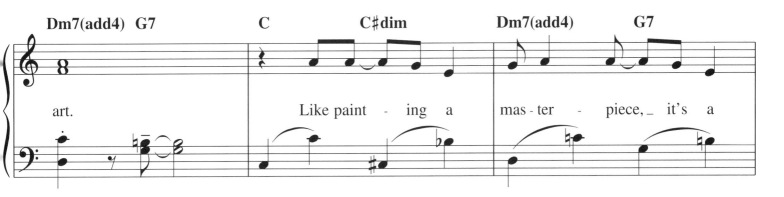

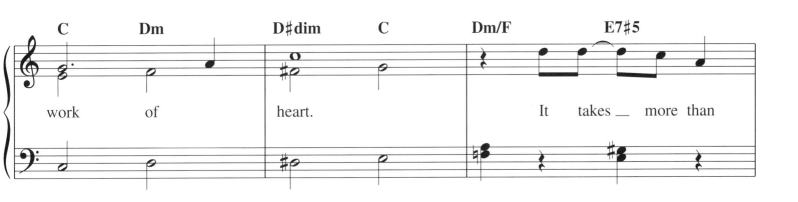

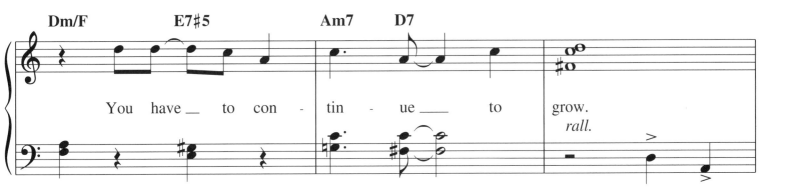

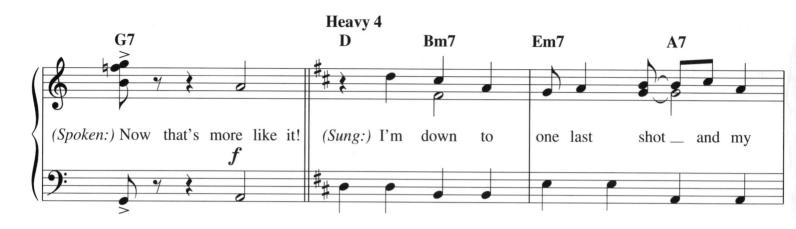

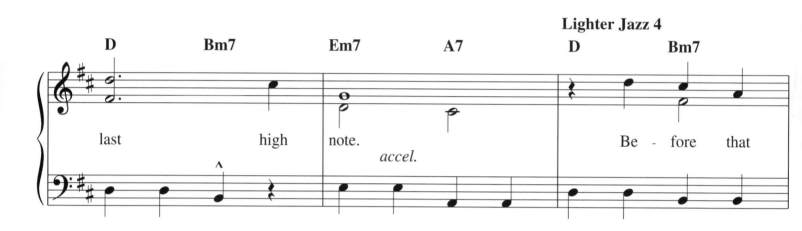

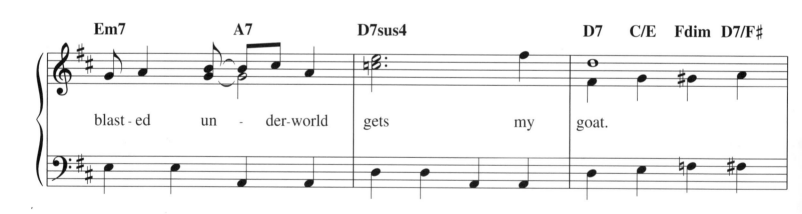

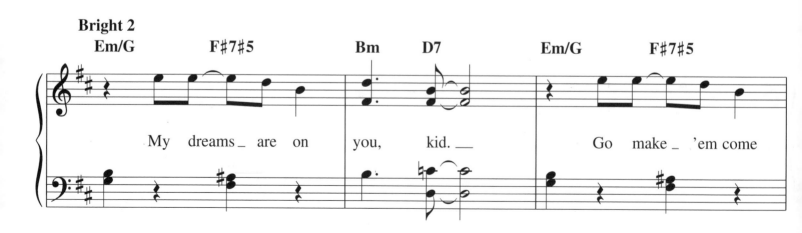

true. Climb that up-hill slope. Keep

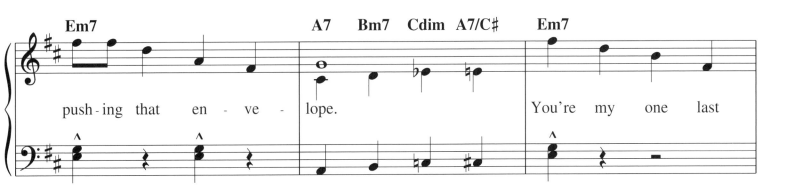

push-ing that en-ve-lope. You're my one last

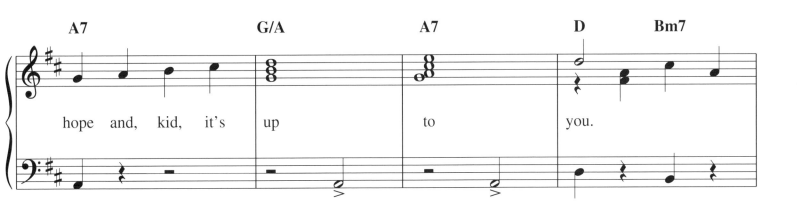

hope and, kid, it's up to you.

ZERO TO HERO

from Walt Disney Pictures' HERCULES

Music by ALAN MENKEN
Lyrics by DAVID ZIPPEL

Driving 4

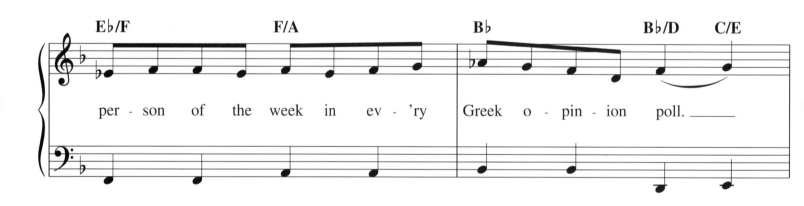

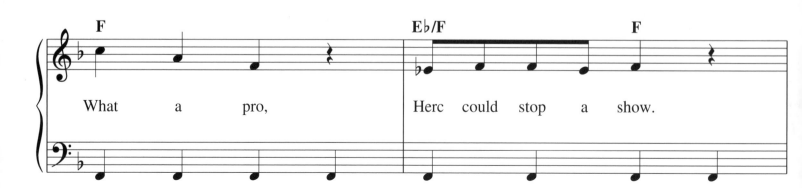

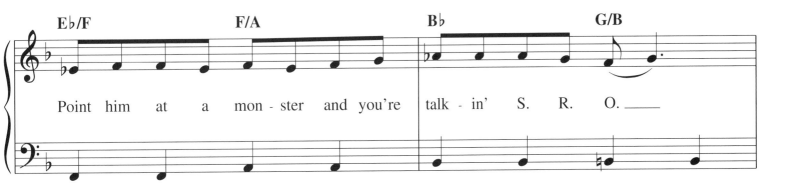

Point him at a mon-ster and you're talk-in' S. R. O. ___

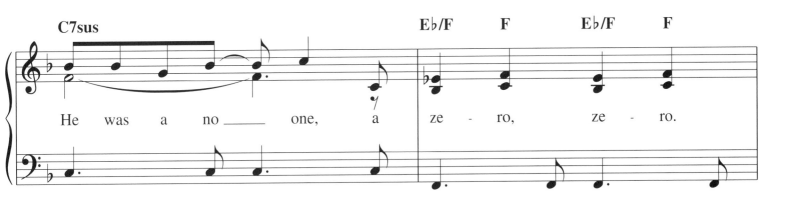

He was a no ___ one, a ze - ro, ze - ro.

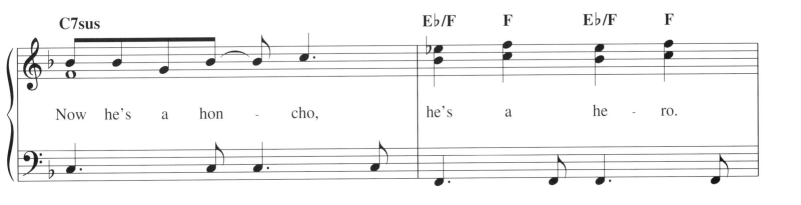

Now he's a hon - cho, he's a he - ro.

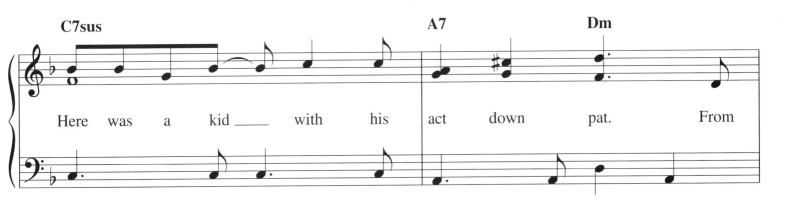

Here was a kid ___ with his act down pat. From

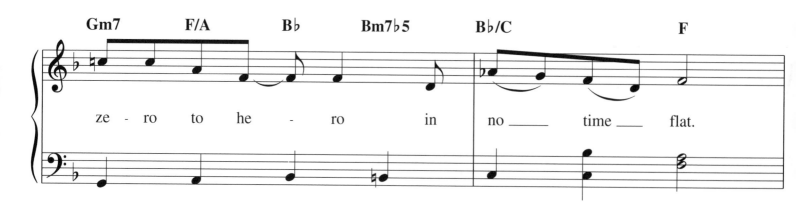

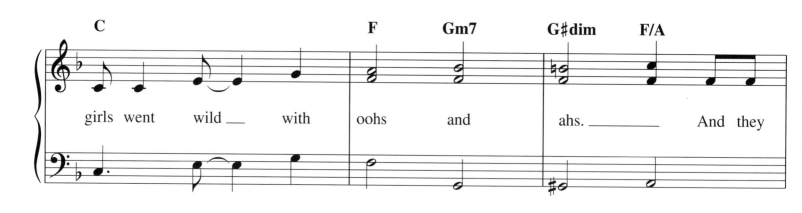

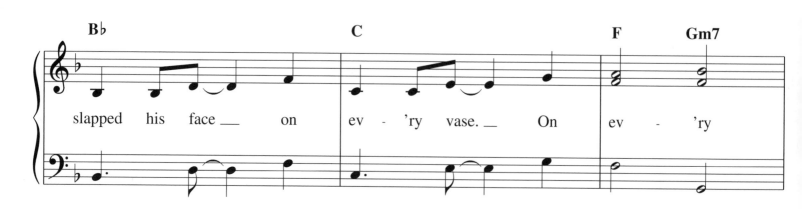

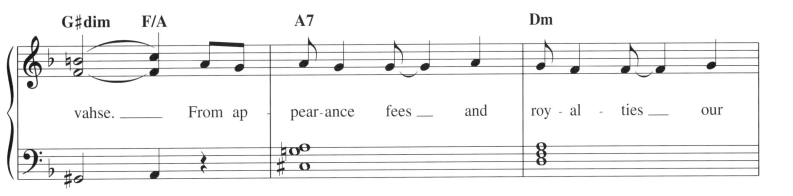

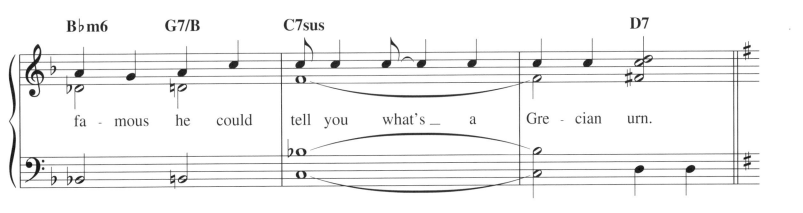

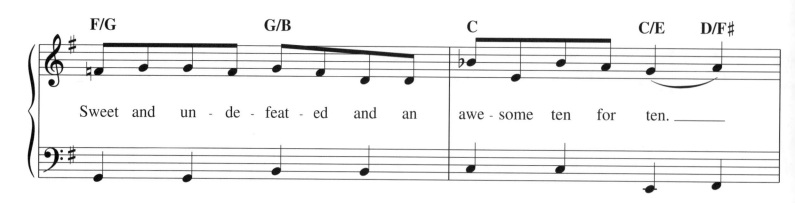

Sweet and un - de - feat - ed and an awe - some ten for ten. _____

Folks lined up just to watch him flex,

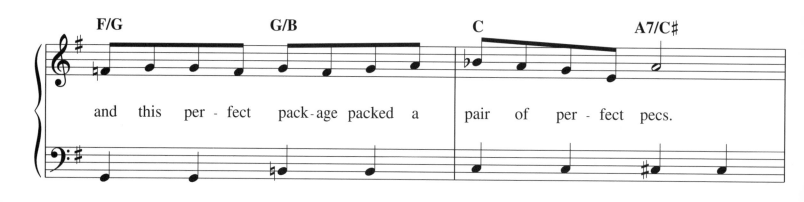

and this per - fect pack - age packed a pair of per - fect pecs.

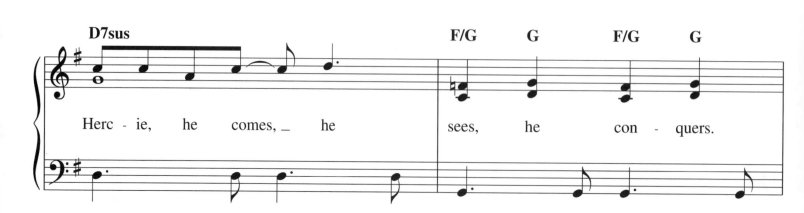

Herc - ie, he comes, _ he sees, he con - quers.

Hon - ey, the crowds __ were go - ing bon - kers.

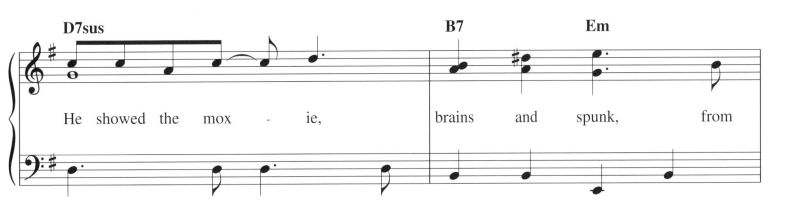

He showed the mox - ie, brains and spunk, from

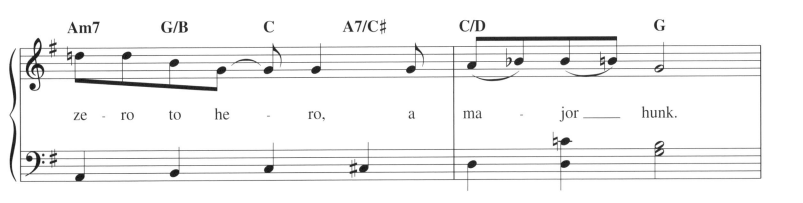

ze - ro to he - ro, a ma - jor ___ hunk.

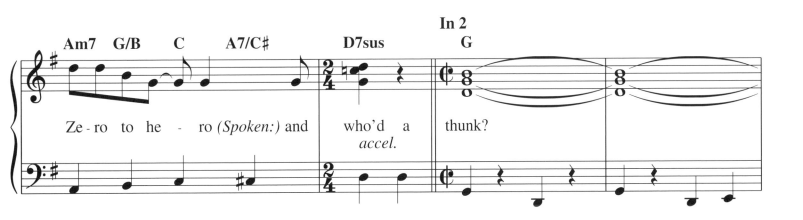

Ze - ro to he - ro *(Spoken:)* and who'd a *accel.* thunk?

(Sung:) Who put the glad in glad - i - a - tor?

Her - cu - les. Whose dar-ing deeds _ are great the - a - ter?

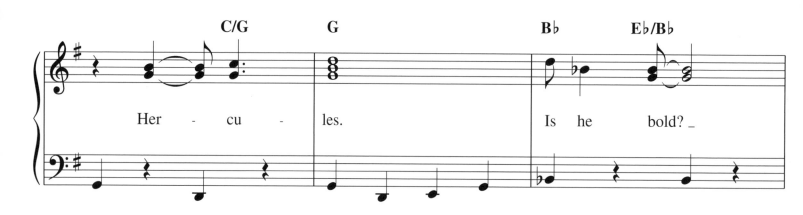

Her - cu - les. Is he bold? _

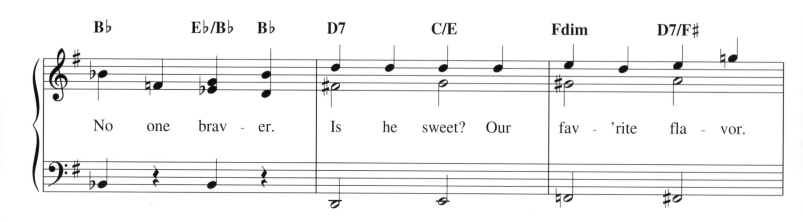

No one brav - er. Is he sweet? Our fav - 'rite fla - vor.

123

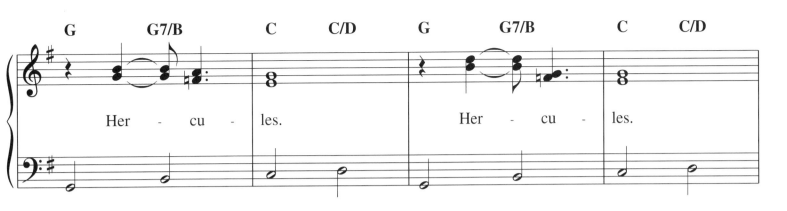

Her - cu - les.   Her - cu - les.

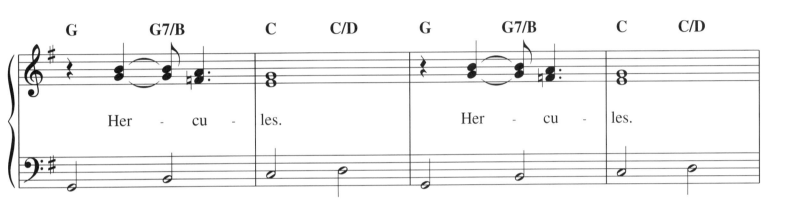

Her - cu - les.   Her - cu - les.

Her - cu - les.   Her - cu - les.

Bless my soul,   Herc was on a roll,   un - de -

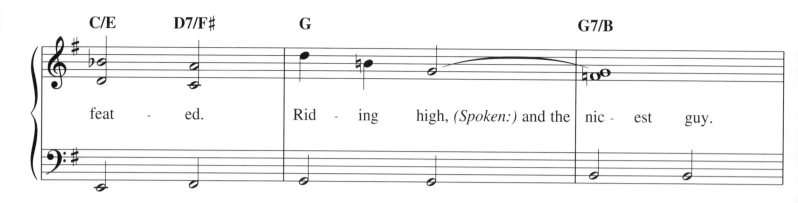

feat - ed. Rid - ing high, *(Spoken:)* and the nic - est guy.

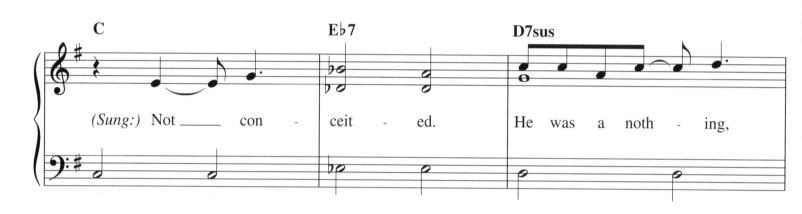

(Sung:) Not ___ con - ceit - ed. He was a noth - ing,

ze - ro, ze - ro. Now he's a hon - cho,

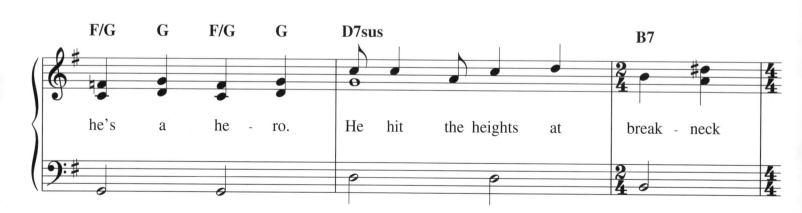

he's a he - ro. He hit the heights at break - neck

speed. From ze - ro to he - ro.

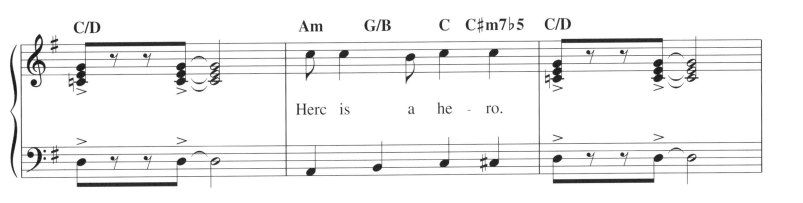

Herc is a he - ro.

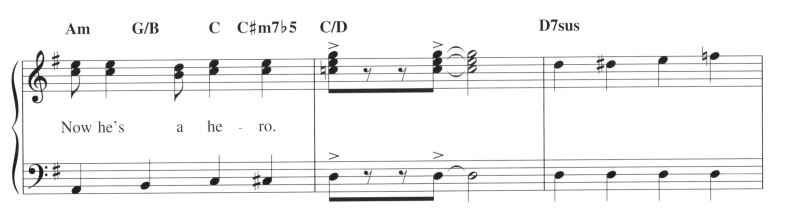

Now he's a he - ro.

(Spoken:)
Yes, in - deed.

GOD HELP THE OUTCASTS
from Walt Disney's THE HUNCHBACK OF NOTRE DAME

Music by ALAN MENKEN
Lyrics by STEPHEN SCHWARTZ

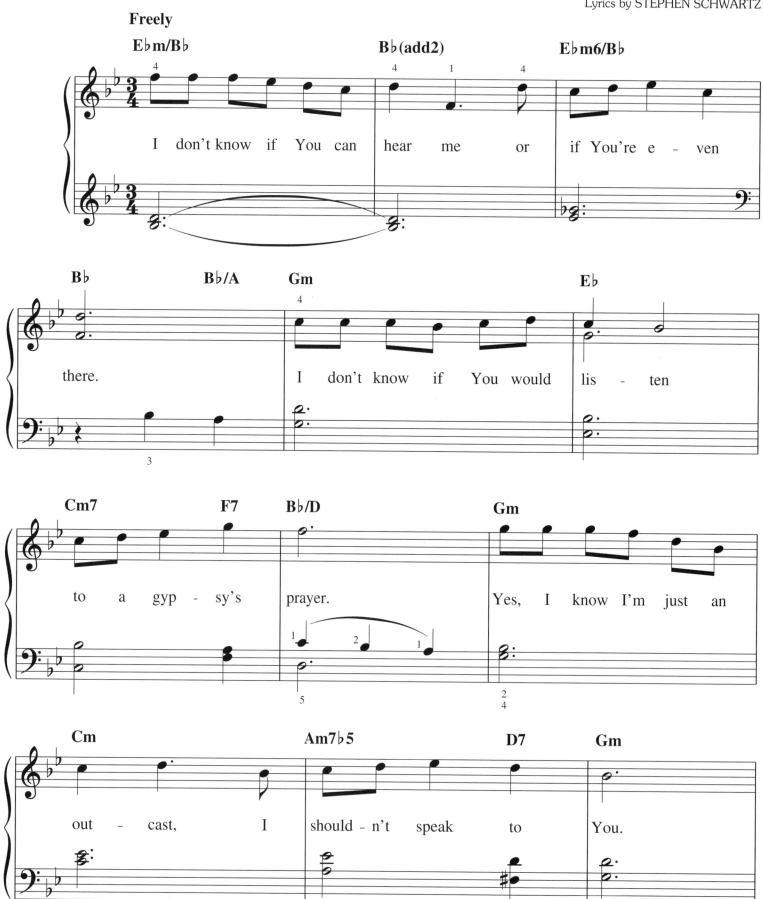

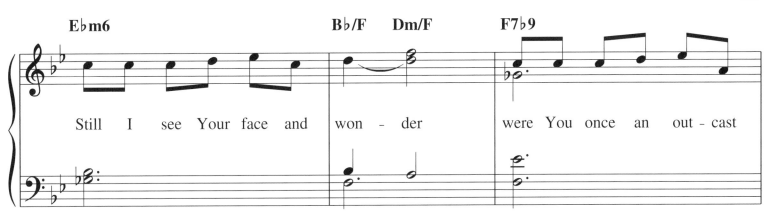

E♭m6

Still I see Your face and won - der

B♭/F Dm/F **F7♭9**

were You once an out - cast

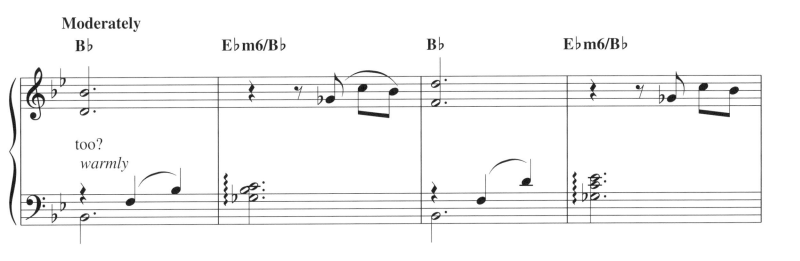

Moderately
B♭   **E♭m6/B♭**   **B♭**   **E♭m6/B♭**

too?
warmly

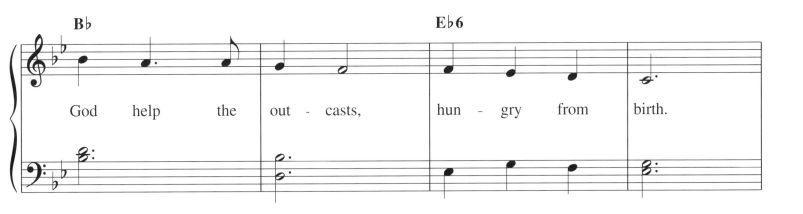

B♭   **E♭6**

God help the out - casts, hun - gry from birth.

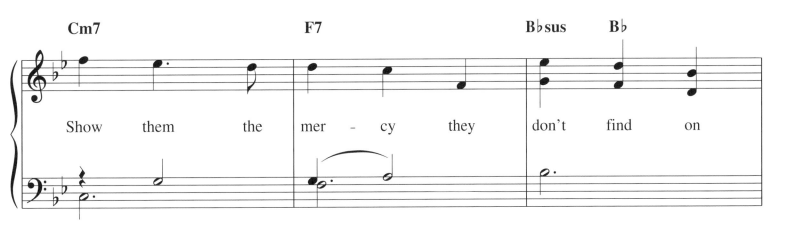

Cm7   **F7**   **B♭sus B♭**

Show them the mer - cy they don't find on

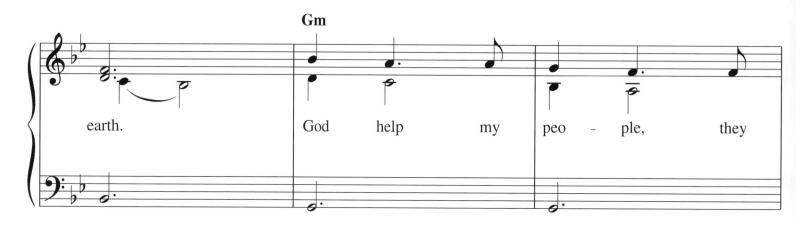

earth. God help my peo - ple, they

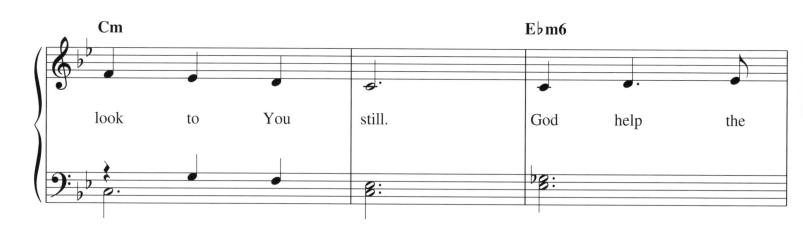

look to You still. God help the

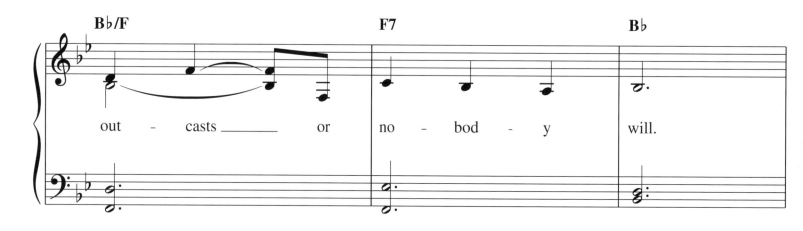

out - casts _____ or no - bod - y will.

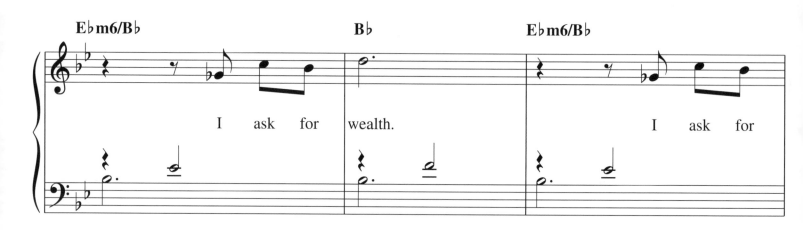

I ask for wealth. I ask for

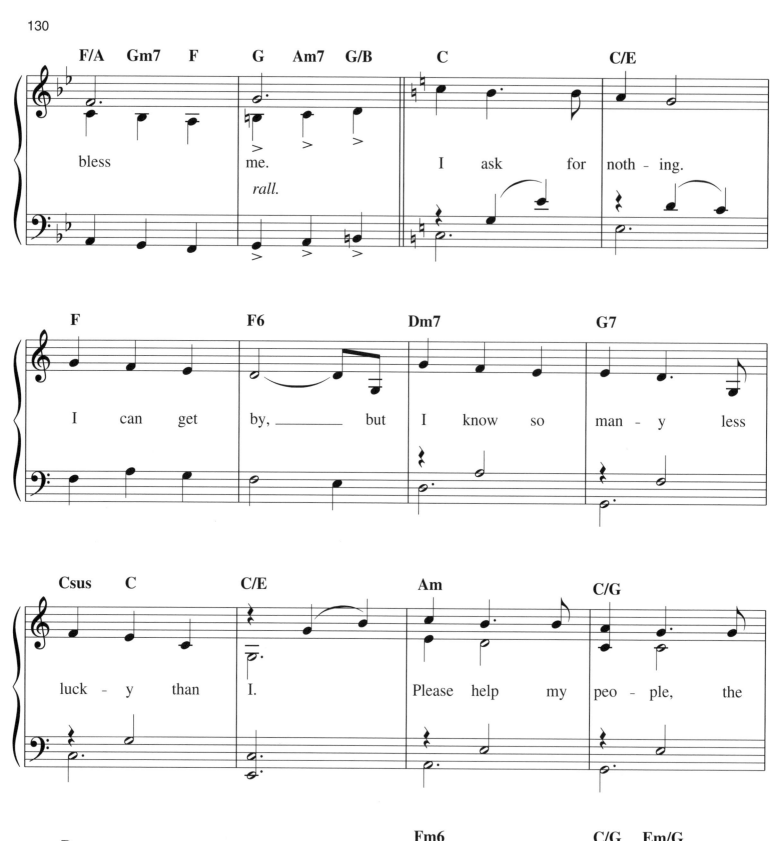

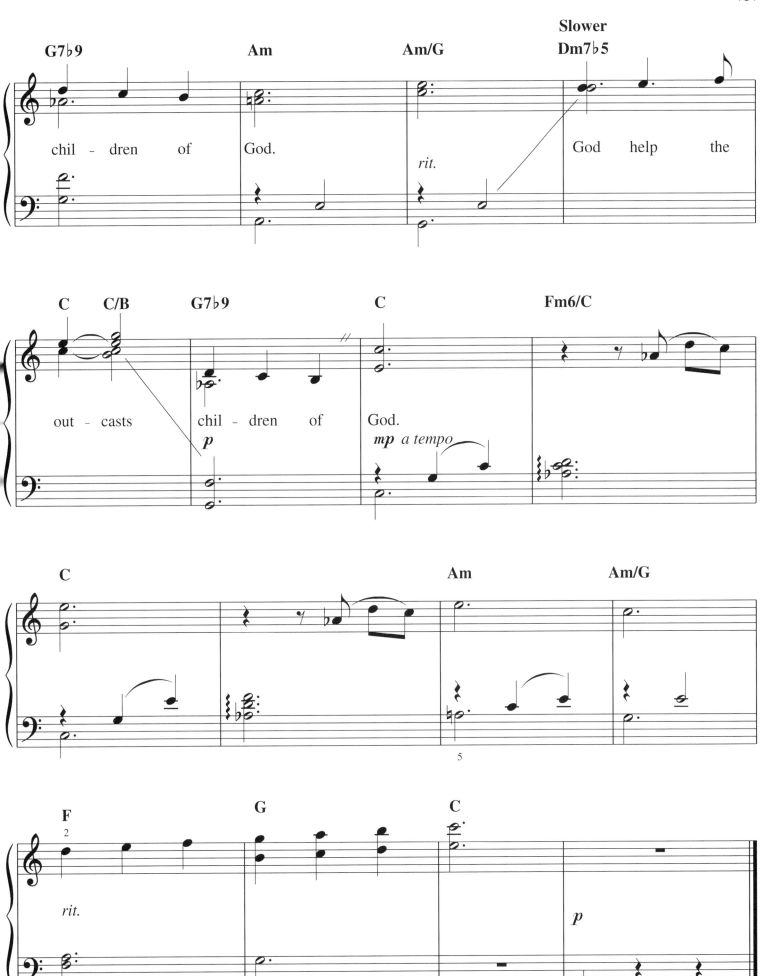

OUT THERE

from Walt Disney's THE HUNCHBACK OF NOTRE DAME

Music by ALAN MENKEN
Lyrics by STEPHEN SCHWARTZ

Moderately, with motion

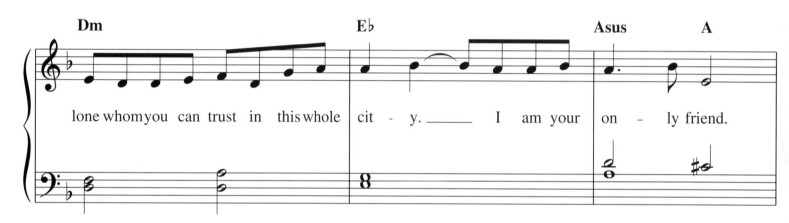

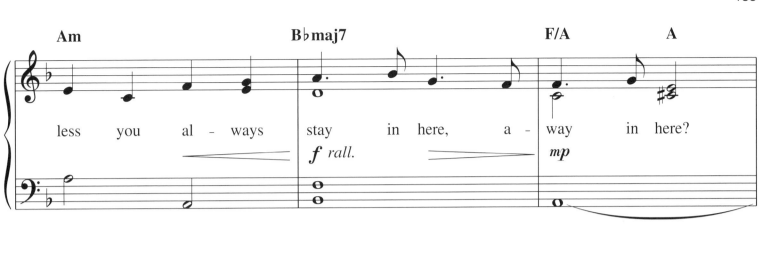

less you al - ways stay in here, a - way in here?

Spoken: Remember what I taught you, Quasimodo. You are de - formed, _____ and you are

plaintive

ug - ly. ____ And these are crimes for which the world shows lit - tle pit - y. ____ You do not

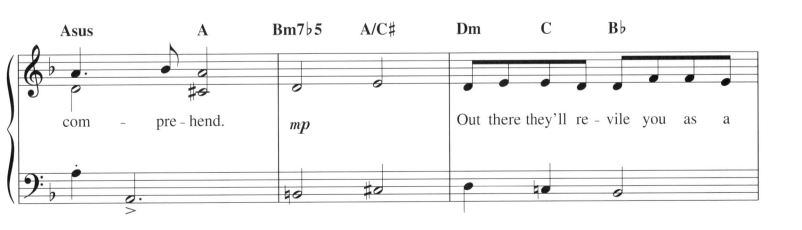

com - pre - hend. Out there they'll re - vile you as a

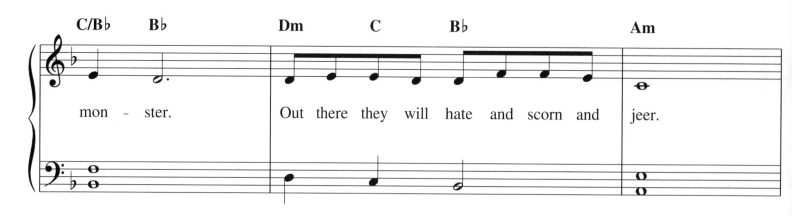

mon - ster. Out there they will hate and scorn and jeer.

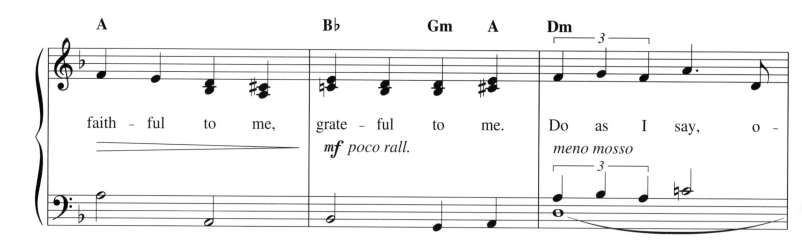

Why in - vite their cal - um - ny and con - ster - na - tion? Stay in here, be

cresc.

ff

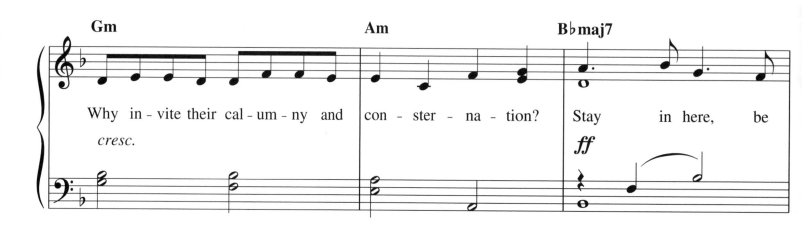

faith - ful to me, grate - ful to me. Do as I say, o -

mf poco rall.

meno mosso

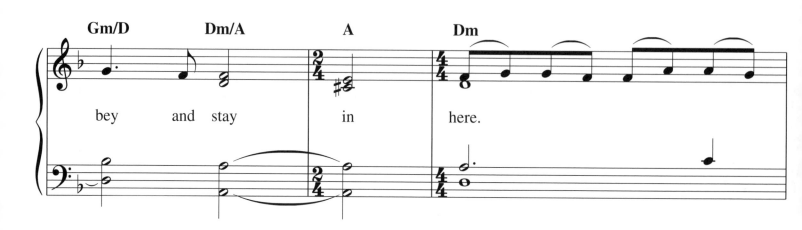

bey and stay in here.

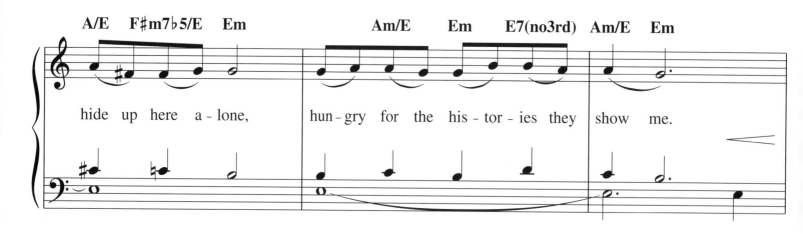

hide up here a - lone, hun - gry for the his - tor - ies they show me.

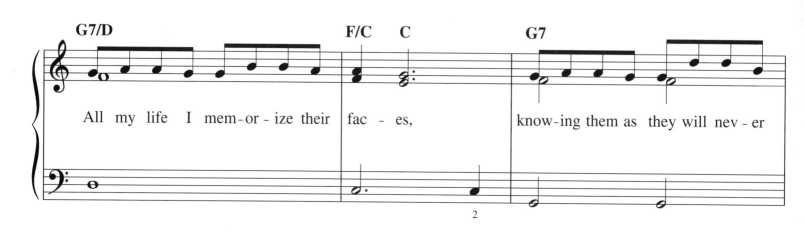

All my life I mem - or - ize their fac - es, know - ing them as they will nev - er

know me. All my life I won - der how it feels to pass a day, not a -

bove them *cresc.* but part of them *rall.* and

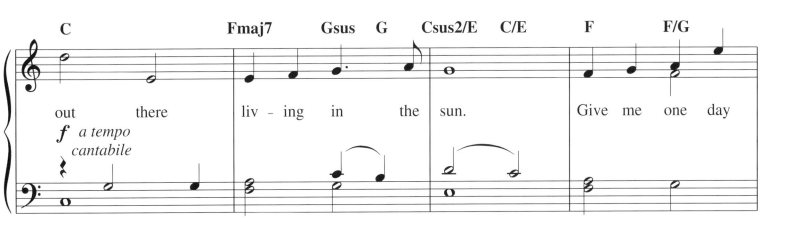

out there   liv - ing in the sun.   Give me one day

f *a tempo*
cantabile

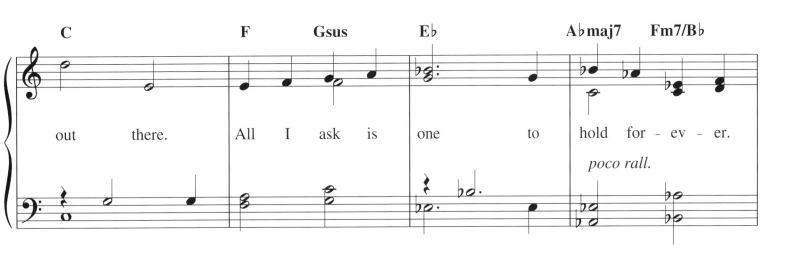

out there.   All I ask is   one   to   hold for - ev - er.

poco rall.

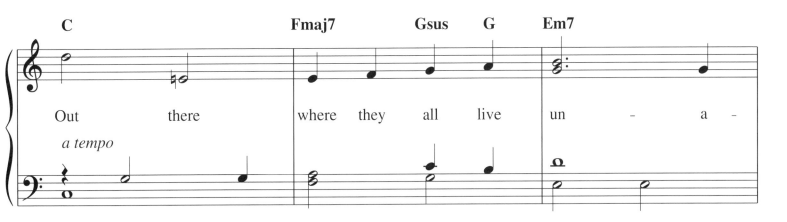

Out there   where they all live   un - a -

a tempo

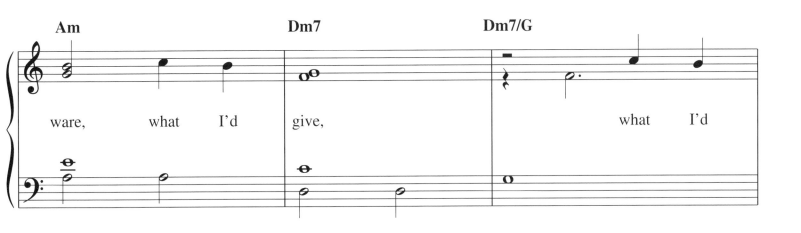

ware,   what I'd give,   what I'd

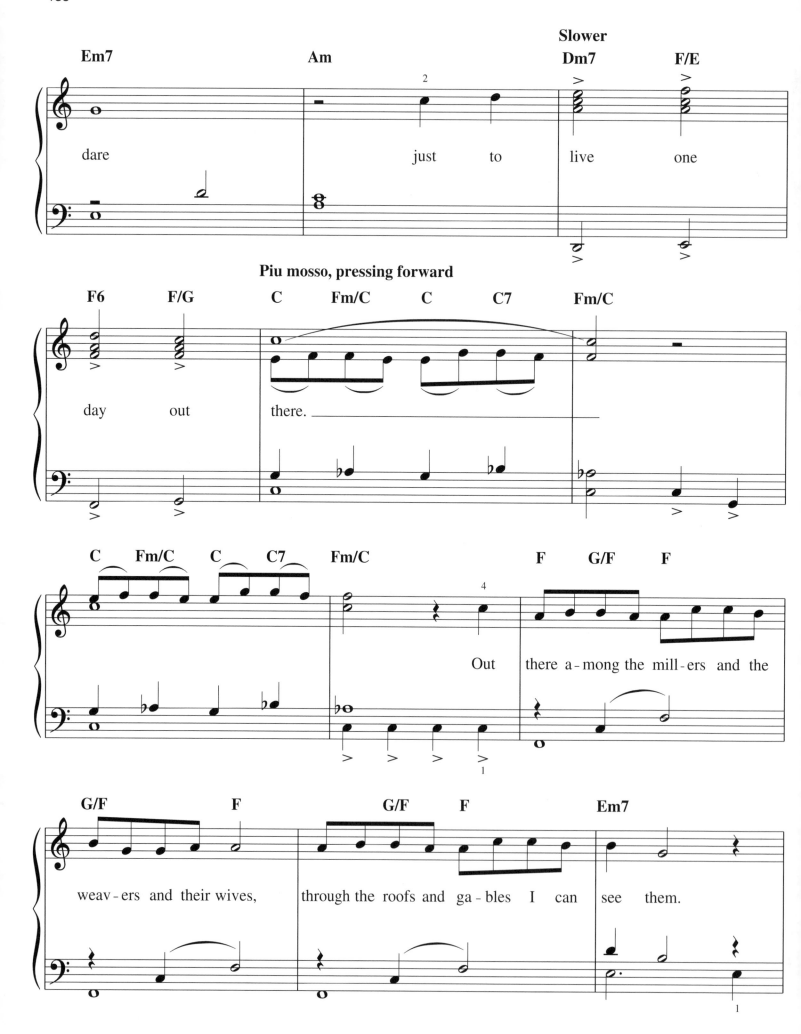

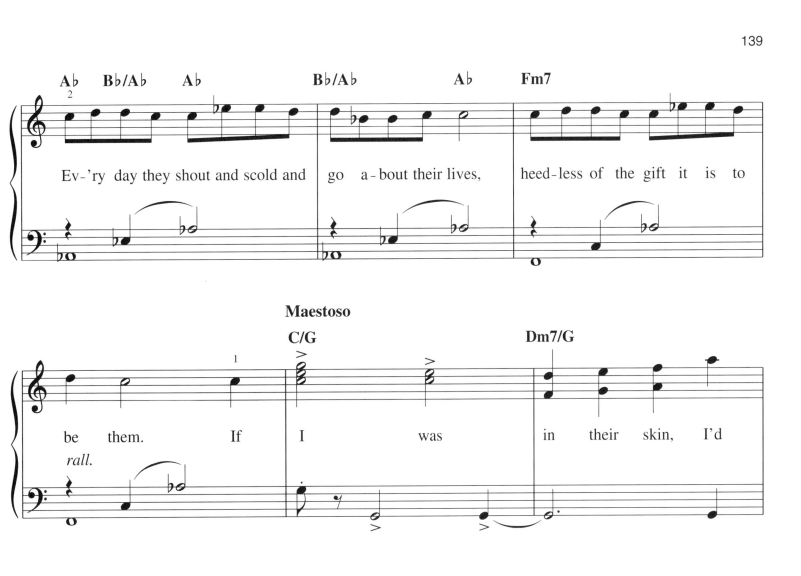

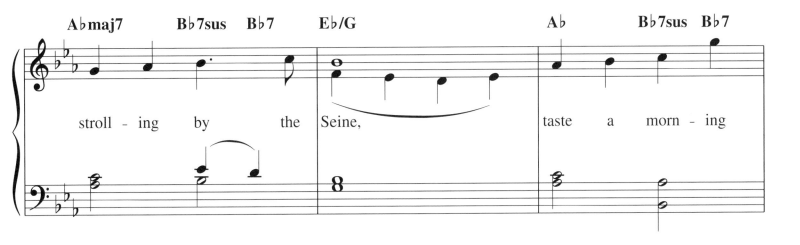

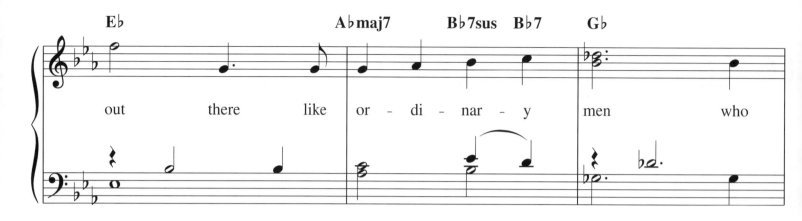

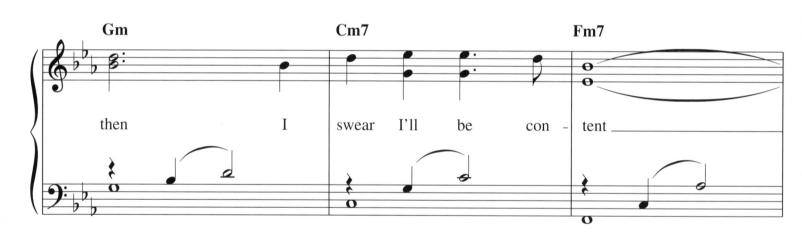

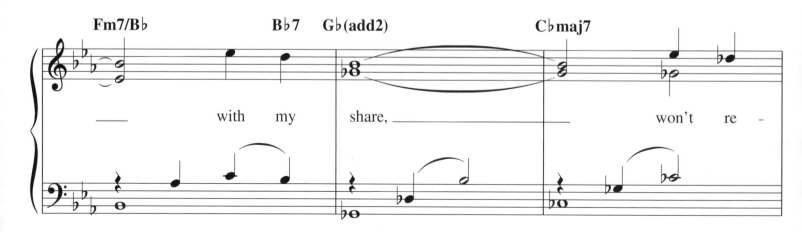

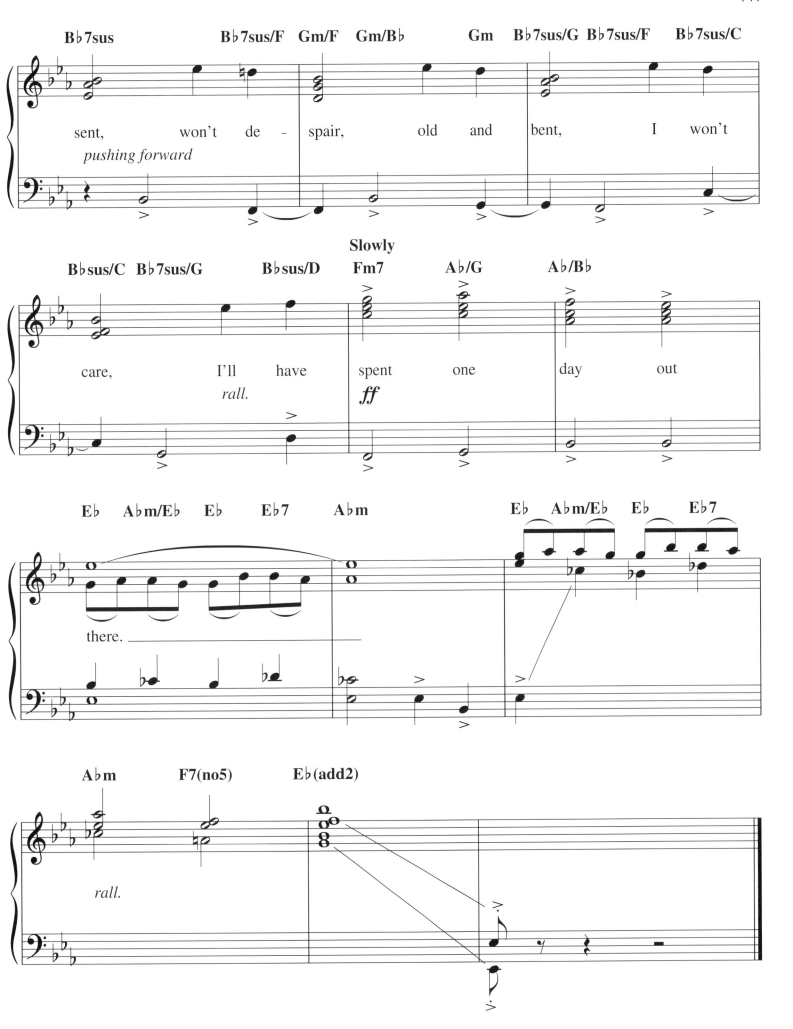

SOMEDAY

from Walt Disney's THE HUNCHBACK OF NOTRE DAME

Music by ALAN MENKEN
Lyrics by STEPHEN SCHWARTZ

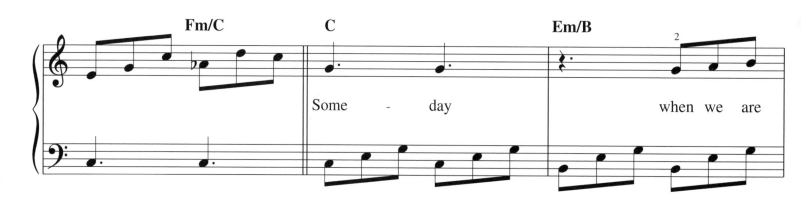

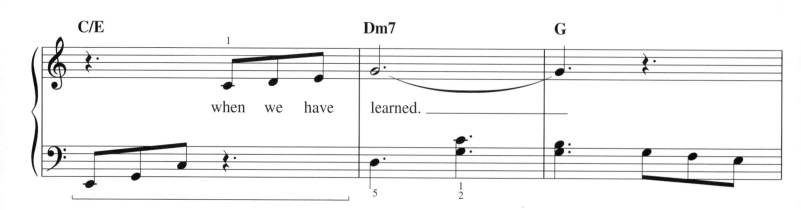

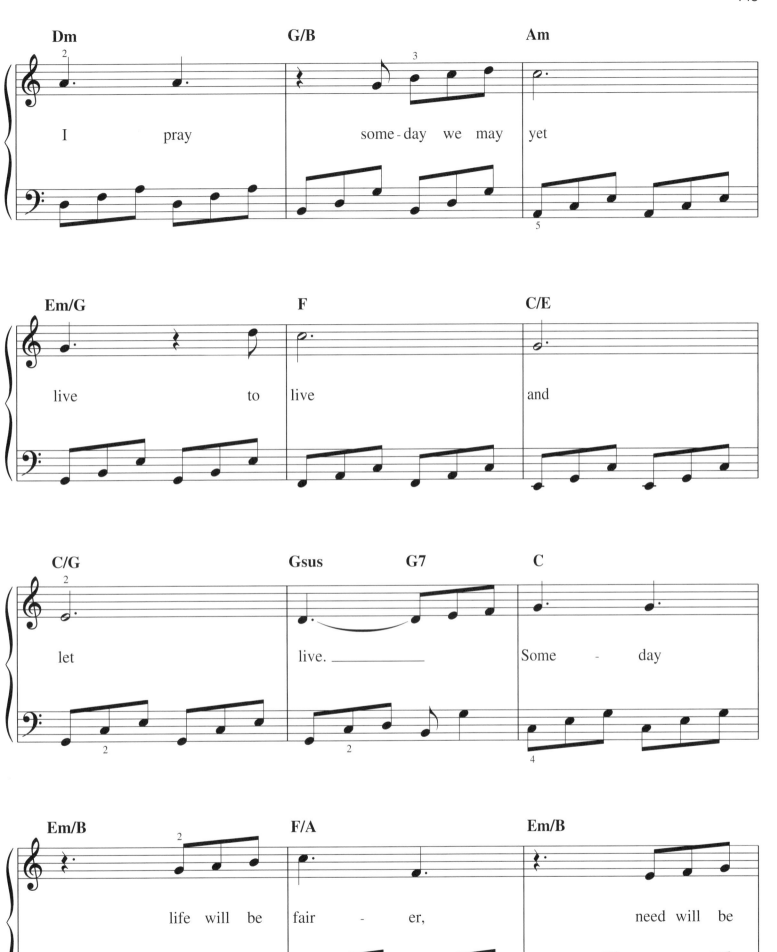

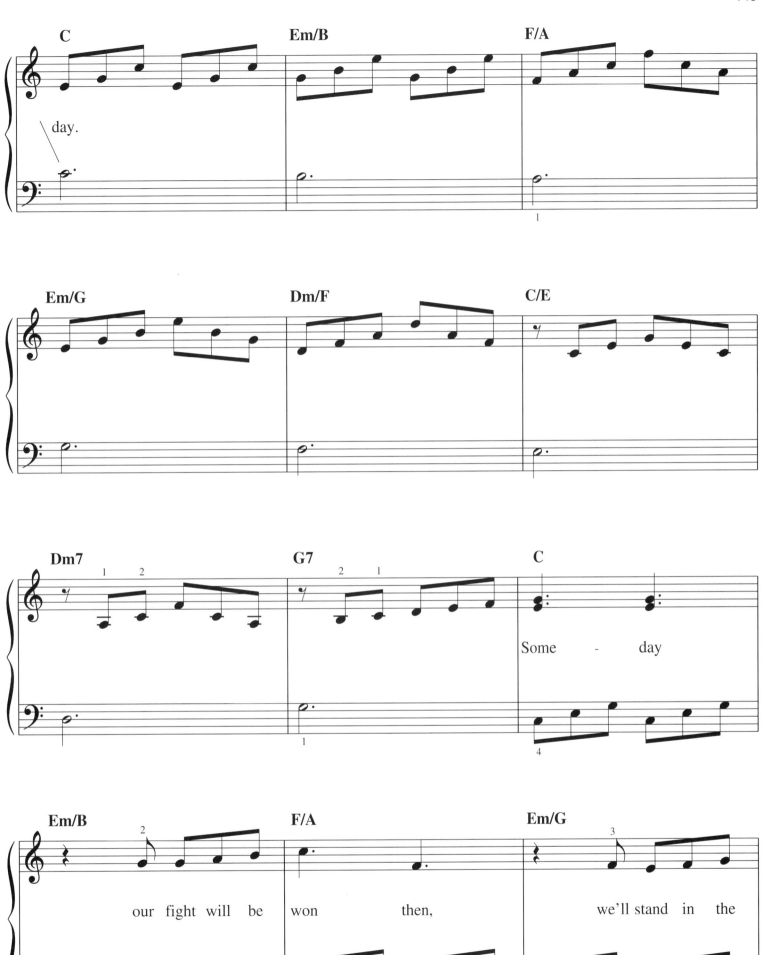

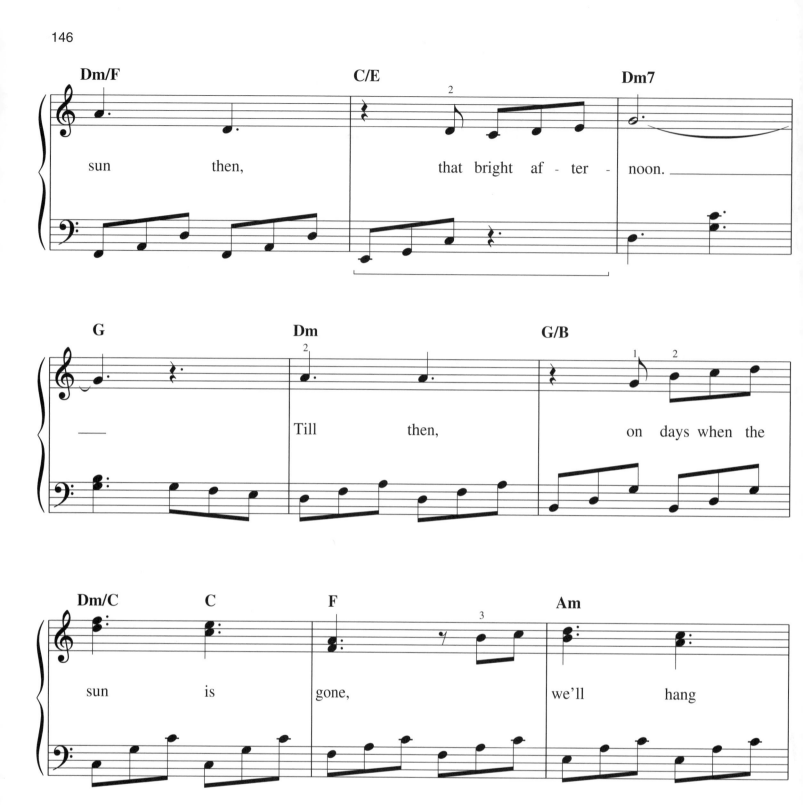

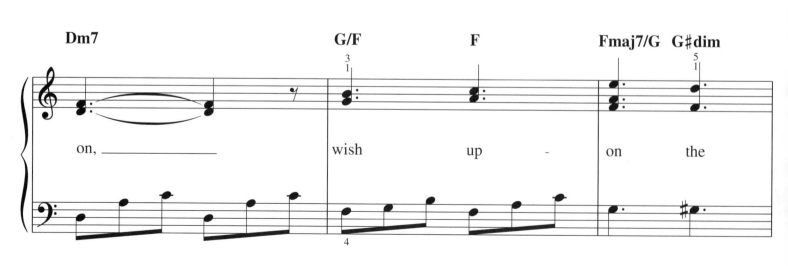

TOPSY TURVY

from Walt Disney's THE HUNCHBACK OF NOTRE DAME

Music by ALAN MENKEN
Lyrics by STEPHEN SCHWARTZ

Once a year   we   throw a par – ty
Here it is,   the   mo – ment you've been

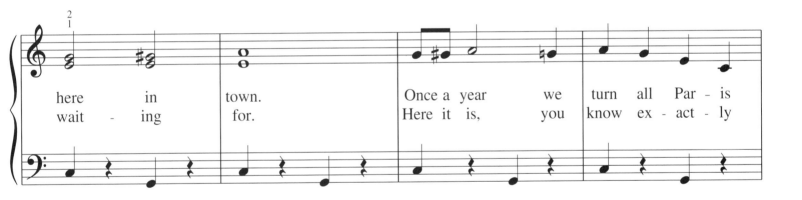

here   in   town.   Once a year   we   turn all Par – is
wait – ing   town.   for.   Here it is,   you   know ex – act – ly

G7   **Dm**

up – side   down.   Ev – 'ry man's   a   king and ev – 'ry
what's   in   store.   Now's the time   we   laugh un – til our

king's   a   clown.
sides   are   sore.
Once a-gain   it's   Top - sy   Tur - vy
Now's the time   we   crown the   King of

C   **F**

Day. _____
Fools! _____
So
It's the day   the   dev - il   in   us
make a face   that's   hor - ri - ble   and

Fm   **C/E**

gets   re -   leased.
fright - en -   ing.
It's the day   we   mock the   prig   and
Make a face   as   grue - some   as   a

E♭dim   **G7sus**

shock   the   priest.
gar - goyle's   wing.
Ev - 'ry-thing   is   top - sy   tur - vy
For the face   that's   ug - li - est   will

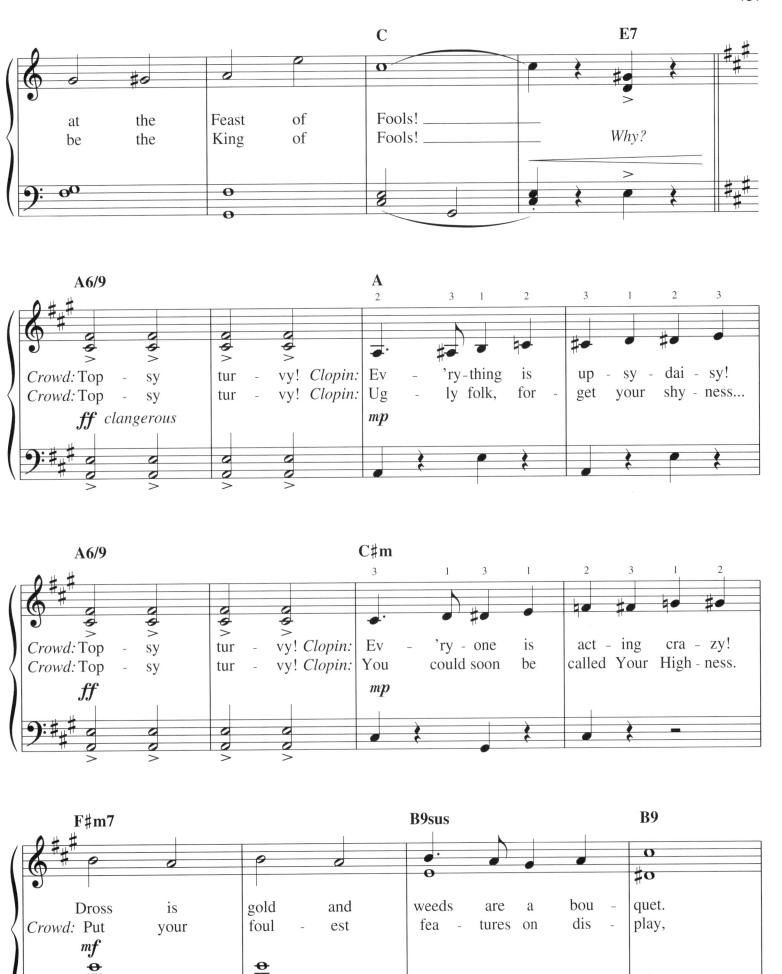

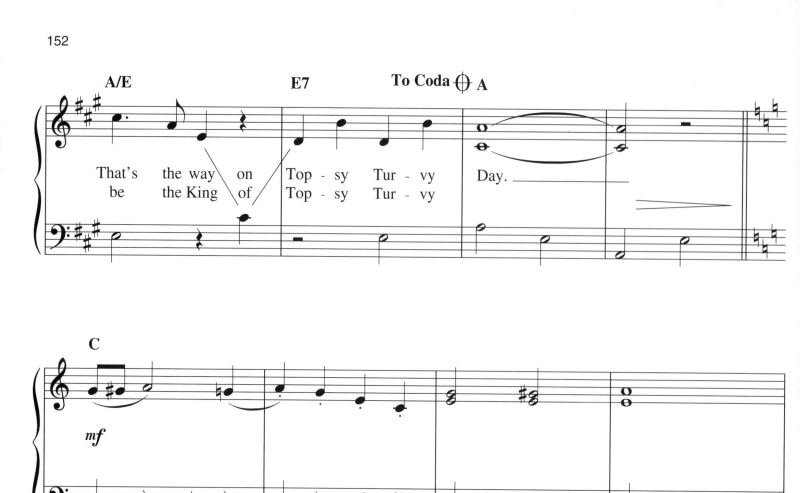

That's the way on Top - sy Tur - vy Day. _____
be the King of Top - sy Tur - vy

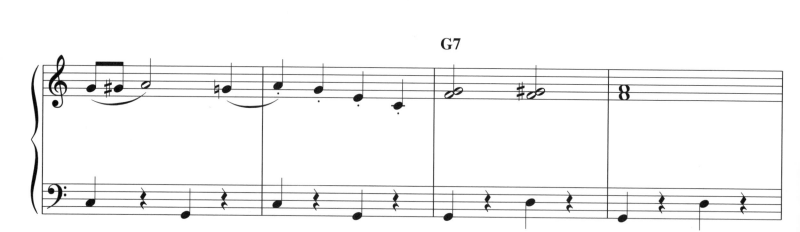

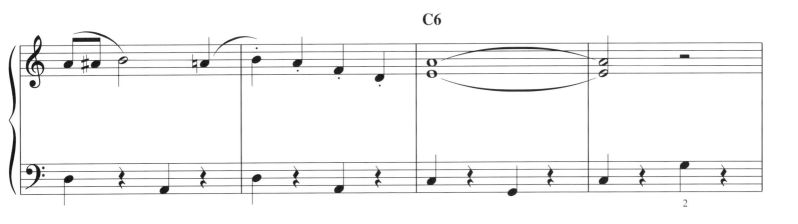

C6

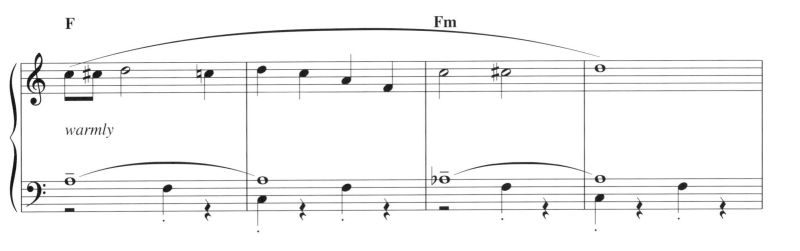

F · · · · · · · · · · · · · · · Fm

warmly

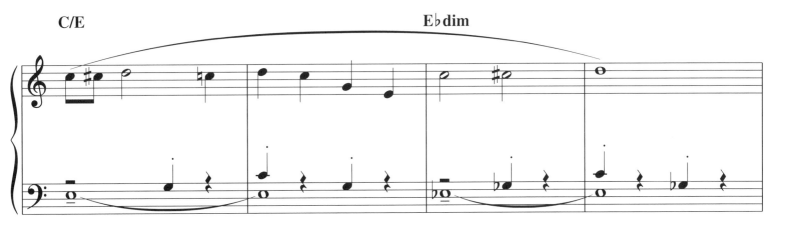

C/E · · · · · · · · · · · · · · · E♭dim

G7

154

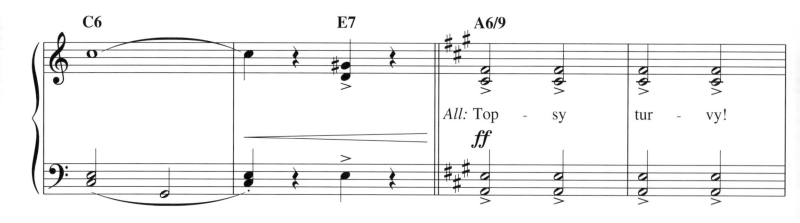

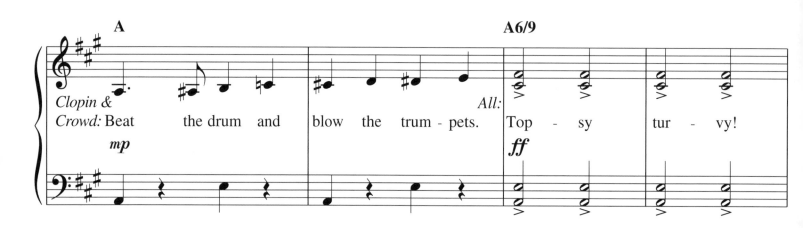

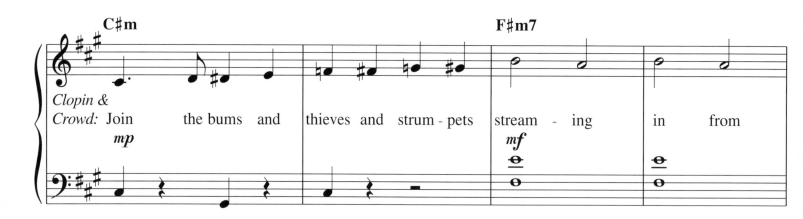

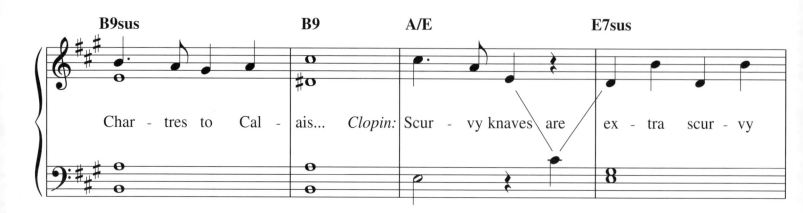

155

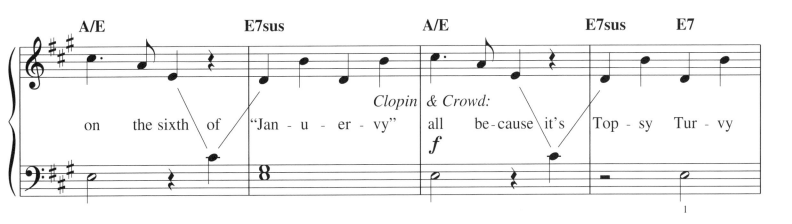

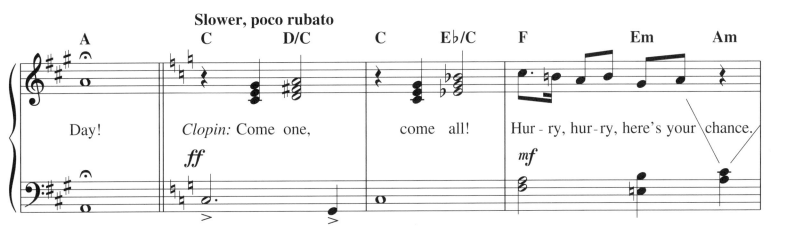

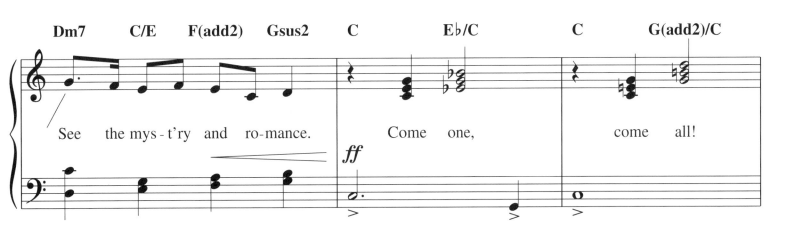

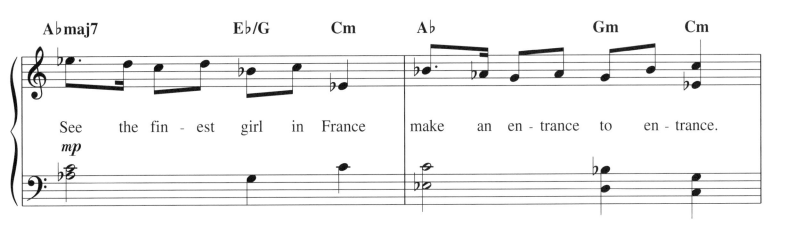

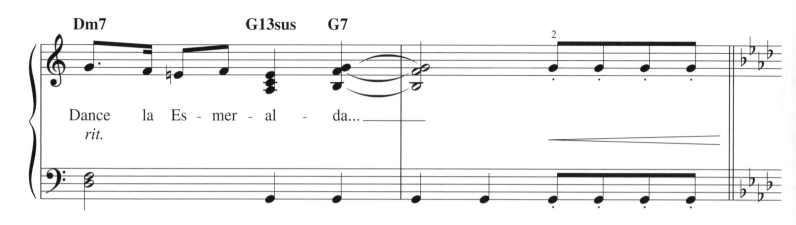

Dm7   G13sus   G7

Dance la Es - mer - al - da...
rit.

Slower
Cm   **Fm**

Dance!
f

C7/F

poco a poco accel.

Fm   **C7/F**   **Fm**   **Db7**

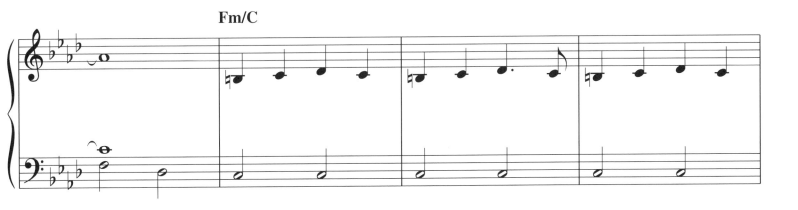

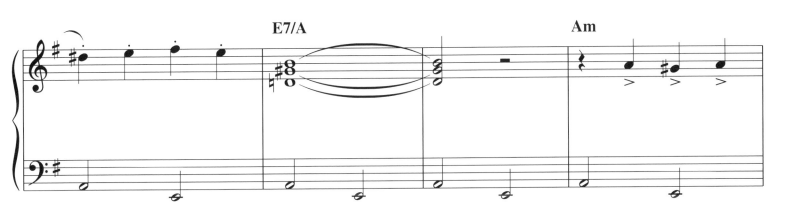

158

159

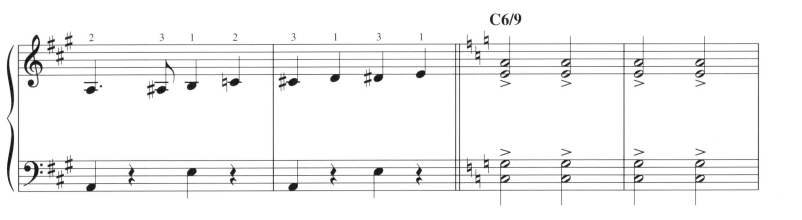

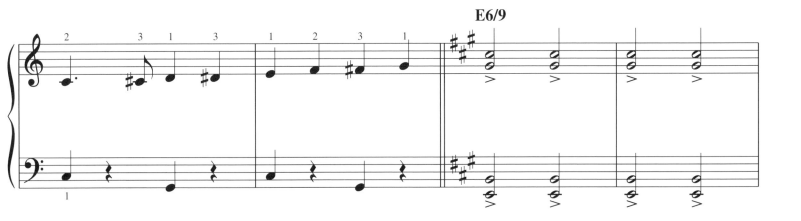

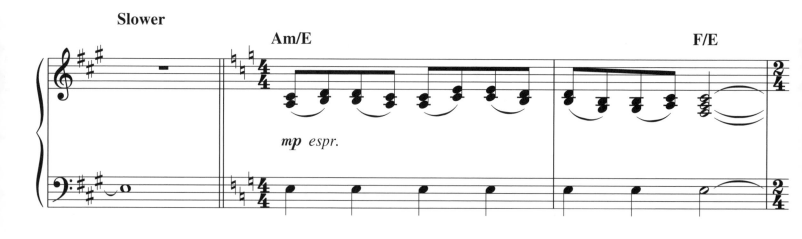

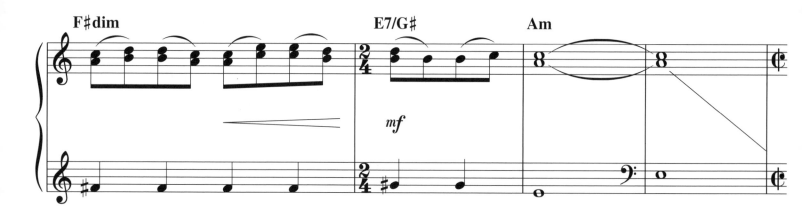

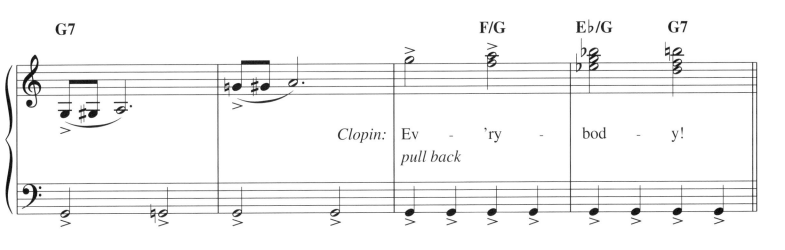

G7 · F/G · E♭/G · G7

Clopin: Ev - 'ry - bod - y!
pull back

Very slow

C

Crowd:
Once a year we throw a par - ty here in town.
poco a poco accel.

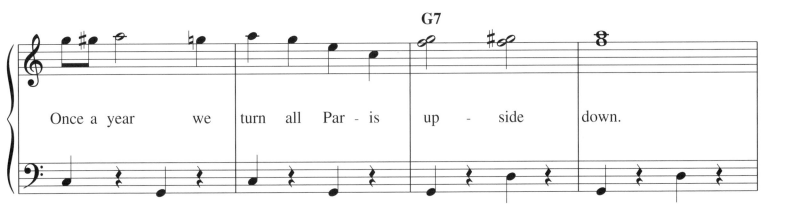

G7

Once a year we turn all Par - is up - side down.

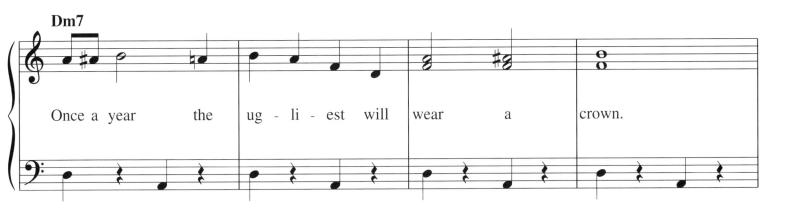

Dm7

Once a year the ug - li - est will wear a crown.

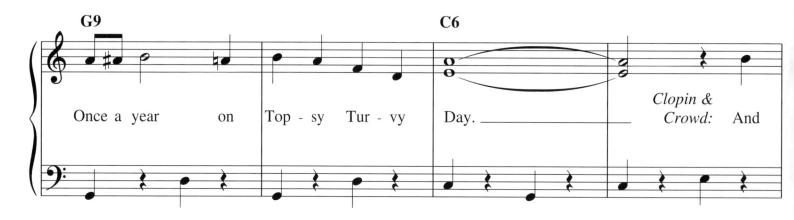

G9   C6

Once a year   on   Top - sy   Tur - vy   Day. _____   *Clopin &*
Crowd: And

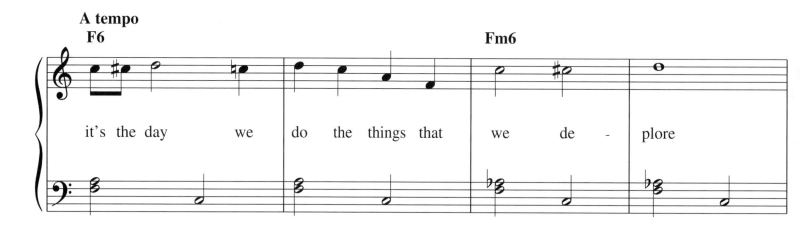

A tempo
F6   Fm6

it's the day   we   do   the   things   that   we   de -   plore

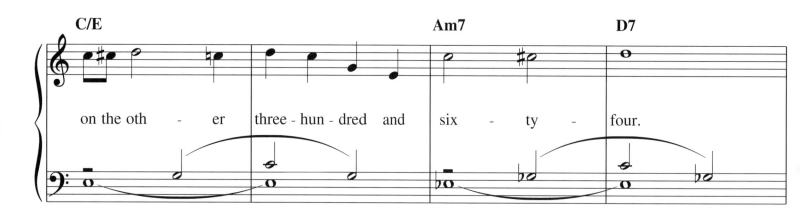

C/E   Am7   D7

on the oth -   er   three - hun - dred   and   six -   ty -   four.

G9sus   G9   G9sus   G9

Once a year   we   love   to   drop   in   where the beer   is   nev - er   stop - pin'

HAWAIIAN ROLLER COASTER RIDE

from Walt Disney's LILO & STITCH

Words and Music by ALAN SILVESTRI
and MARK KEALI'I HO'OMALU

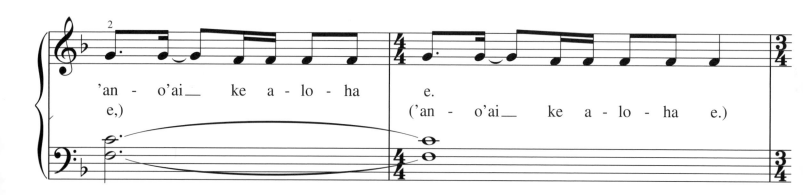

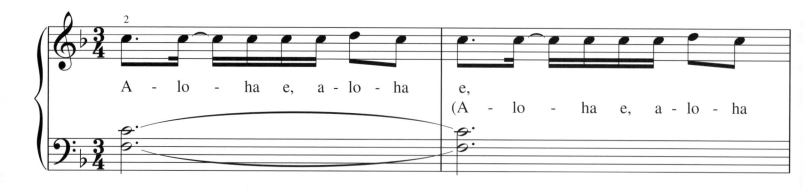

Lead:
1.,3. There's no___ place I'd rath - er be

*Chorus:
than on my surf - board out at sea.

All:
2. There's no___ place I'd rath - er be

Chorus:
than on the sea - shore dry, wet, free.

*Children's chorus

Lead: Lin - ger - ing in the o - cean blue.
All: On gold - en sand is where I'd lay,

Chorus: *Lead:*
And if I had one wish come true I'd
Chorus: *All:*
and if I on - ly had my way, I'd

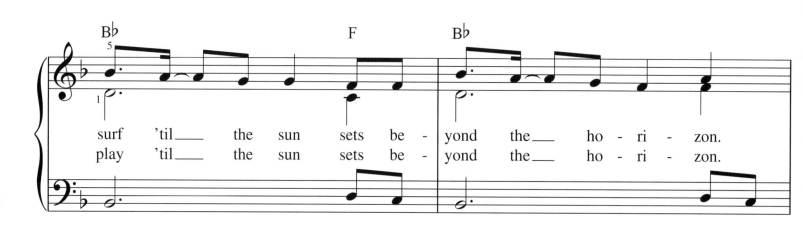

surf 'til___ the sun sets be - yond the___ ho - ri - zon.
play 'til___ the sun sets be - yond the___ ho - ri - zon.

Chorus: A - wi - ki - wi - ki, mai lo hi lo hi.
Chorus: La - la - la i ka la ha - na - ha - na.

La - we mai i ko pa - pa he -'e na - lu.
Me ke kai ho - en e i ka pu -'e o - ne.

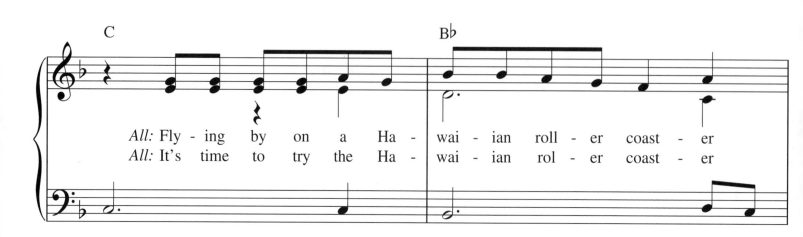

All: Fly - ing by on a Ha - wai - ian roll - er coast - er
All: It's time to try the Ha - wai - ian rol - er coast - er

F   Gm   F

ride.
ride.

Lead: A - wi - ki - wi - ki, mai lo - hi - lo - hi.
All: Hang loose, hang ten, how's it shake - a - shak - a.

Bb6

Chorus: La - we mai i ko pa - pa he - 'e na - lu.
No wor - ry, no fear. Ain't__ no big - gy, brah - da.

F

Lead: Pi' - i na lu - lu la la - ha - la - ha.
Put - tin' in, cut - tin' up, cut - tin' back, cut - tin' out.

To Coda ⊕

Chorus: O ka mo - a - na ha - nu - pa - nu - pa.
Front side, back side, goof - y foot - ed wipe out.

1.

Lead: La - la - la i ka la ha - na - ha - na.
Chorus: Me ke kai ho - en - e i ka pu - 'e one.

Lead: He - le - he - le mai ka - kou e.
Chorus: Ha - wai - ian roll - er coast - er ride.

2.

Let's go jump - in', surf's up and pump - in'. Coast - in' with the mo - tion of the o - cean.

F

N.C.

Chorus:

Whirl - pools swirl - ing, cas - cad - ing swirl - ing. Ha - wai - ian roll - er coast - er ride.

D.S. al Coda

F

Gm

F

Gm

CODA

C

B♭

Lead:

La - la - la i ka la ha - na - ha - na.

Chorus:

Me ke kai ho - en - e i ka pu - 'e one.

F

Lead:

He - le - he - le mai ka - kou e.

Chorus:

Ha - wai - ian roll - er coast - er ride.

BE PREPARED
from Walt Disney Pictures' THE LION KING

Music by ELTON JOHN
Lyrics by TIM RICE

Steadily, rhythmically

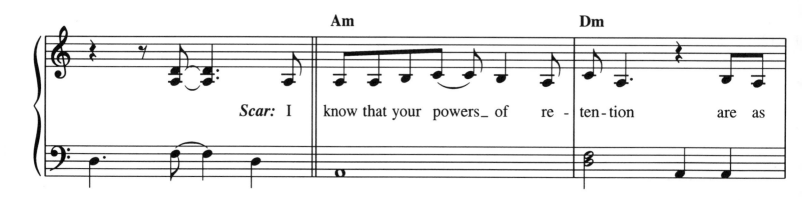

Scar: I know that your powers_ of re - ten - tion are as

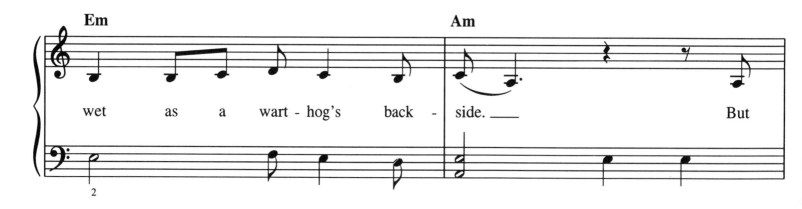

wet as a wart - hog's back - side. ___ But

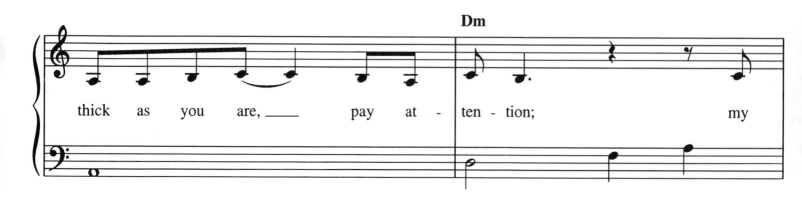

thick as you are, ___ pay at - ten - tion; my

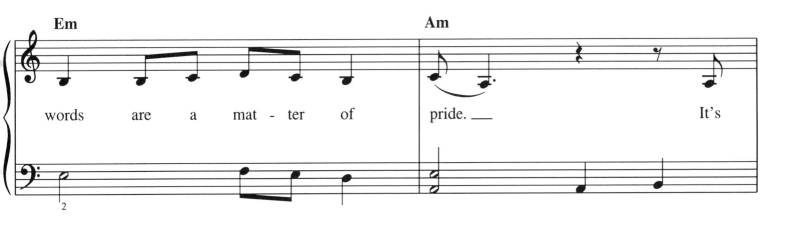

Em   **Am**

words   are   a   mat - ter   of   pride. ___   It's

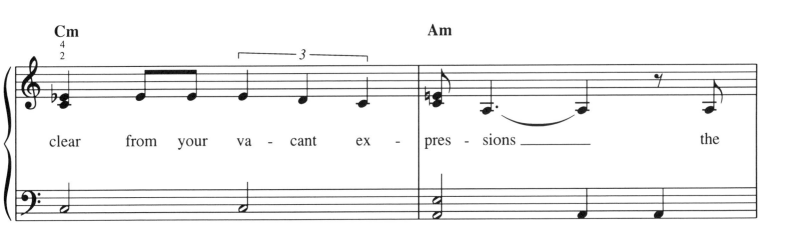

Cm   **Am**

clear   from   your   va - cant   ex -   pres - sions _____   the

Cm   **Am**

lights   are   not   all   on   up -   stairs.   But

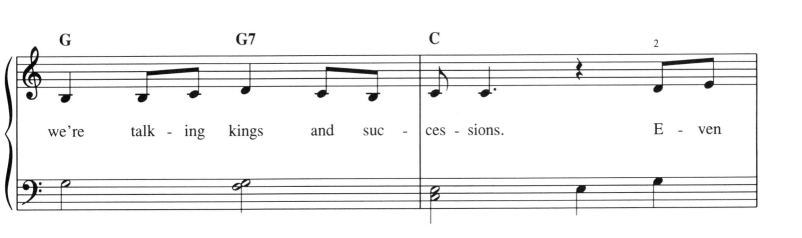

G   **G7**   **C**

we're   talk - ing   kings   and   suc -   ces - sions.   E - ven

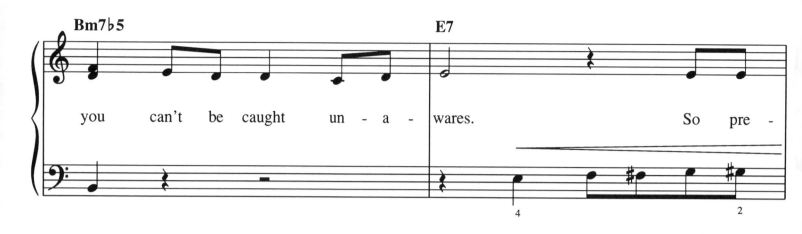

you can't be caught un - a - wares. So pre -

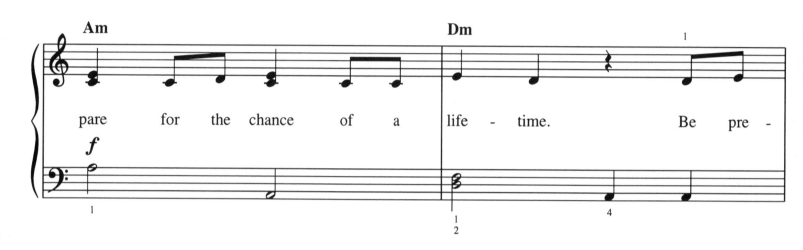

pare for the chance of a life - time. Be pre -

pared for sen - sa - tion - al news. A

shin - ing new e - ra is tip - toe - ing near - er. *And*

Shenzi: *(Spoken:)*

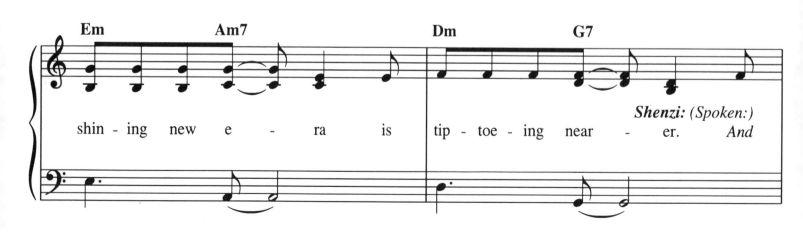

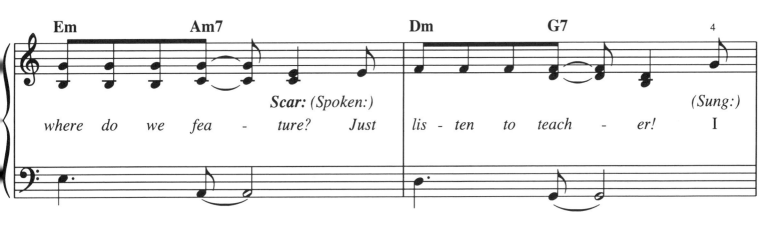

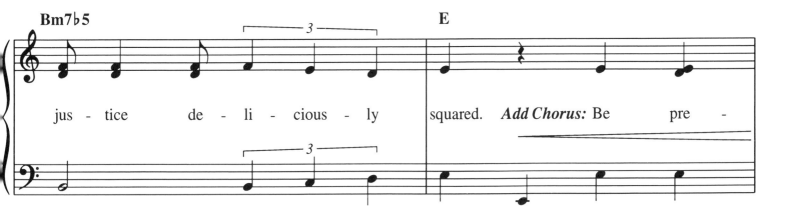

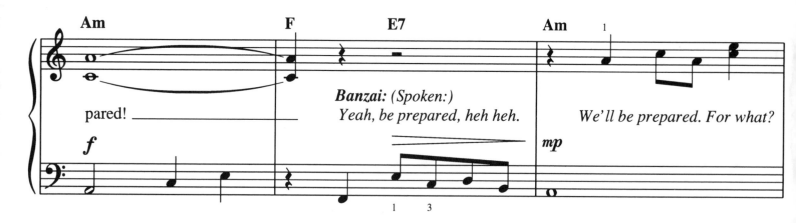

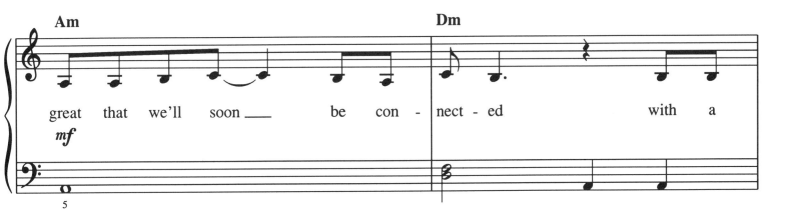

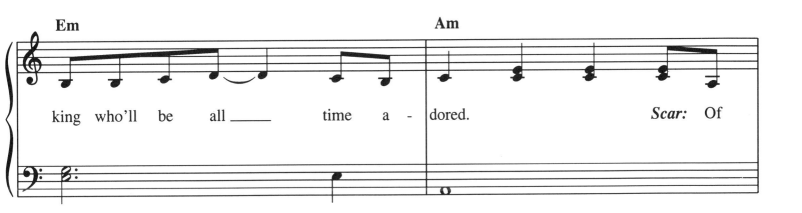

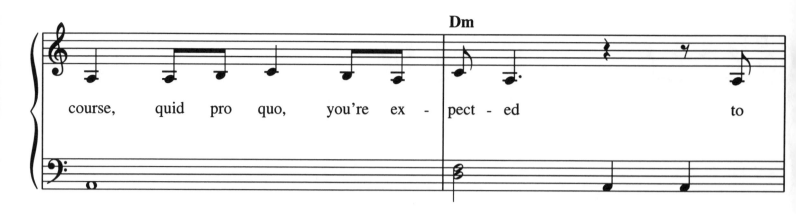

course, quid pro quo, you're ex - pect - ed   to

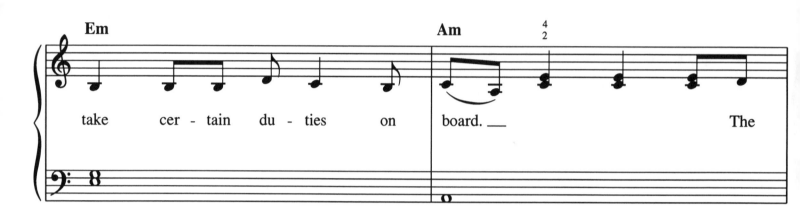

take   cer - tain du - ties   on   board. ___   The

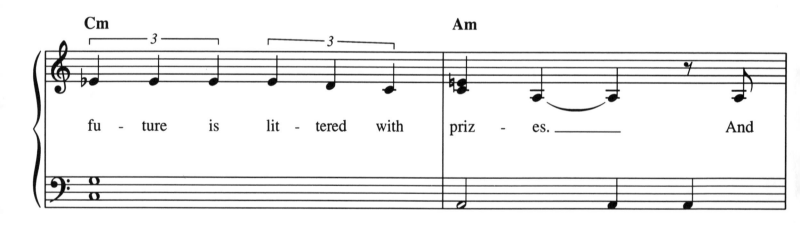

fu - ture is lit - tered with   priz - es. _____   And

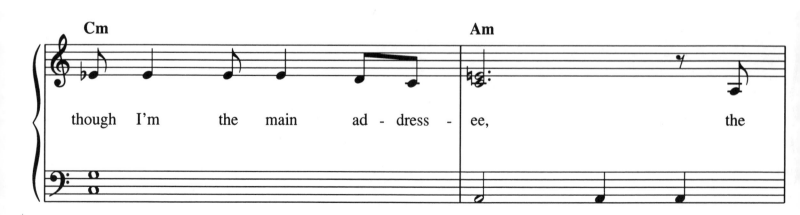

though I'm   the   main   ad - dress - ee,   the

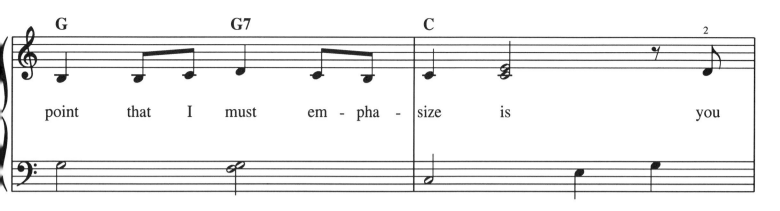

point that I must em - pha - size is you

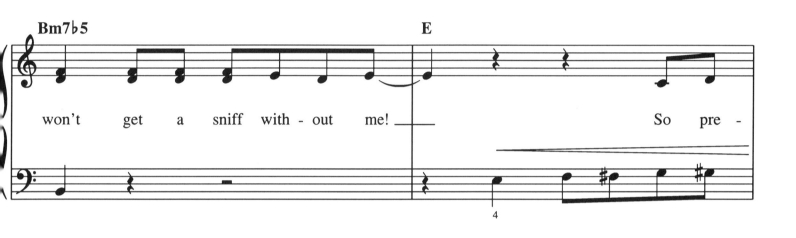

won't get a sniff with - out me! So pre -

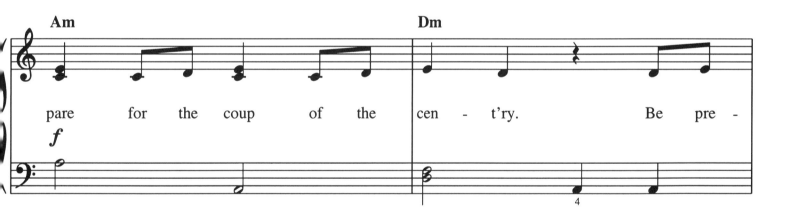

pare for the coup of the cen - t'ry. Be pre -

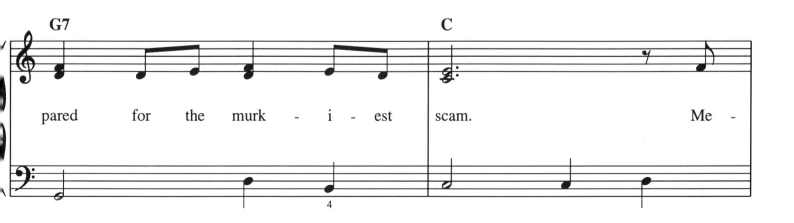

pared for the murk - i - est scam. Me -

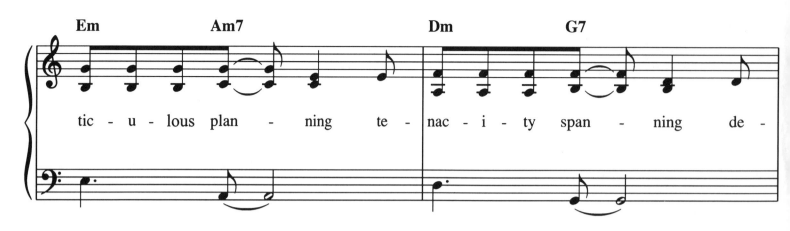

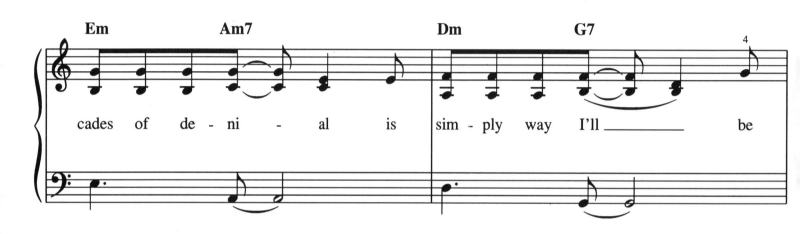

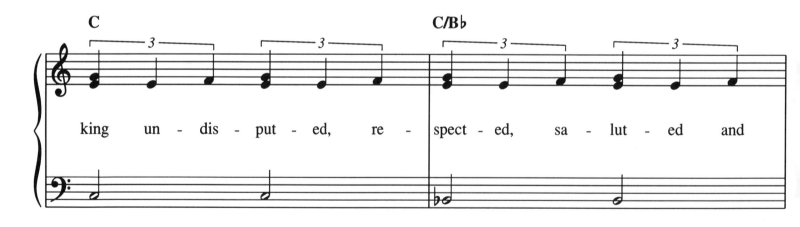

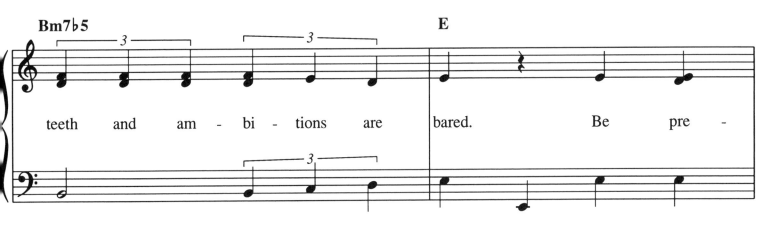

teeth and am - bi - tions are bared. Be pre -

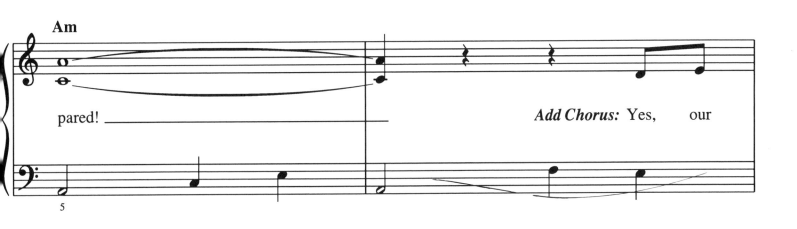

pared! _____ *Add Chorus:* Yes, our

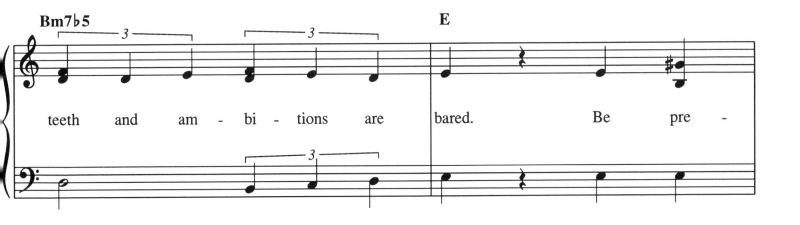

teeth and am - bi - tions are bared. Be pre -

pared!

Wild laughter
molto rit.

CAN YOU FEEL THE LOVE TONIGHT

from Walt Disney Pictures' THE LION KING

Music by ELTON JOHN
Lyrics by TIM RICE

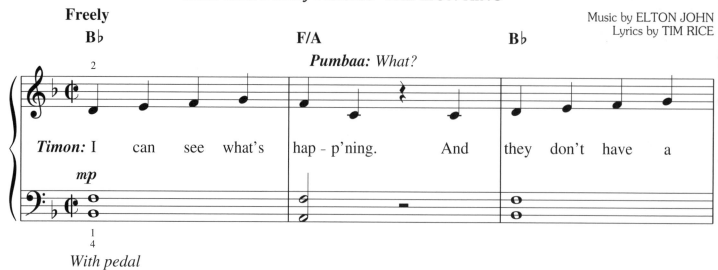

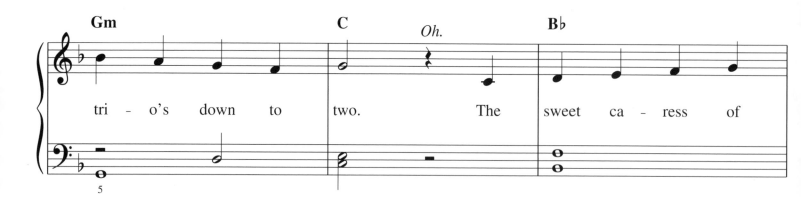

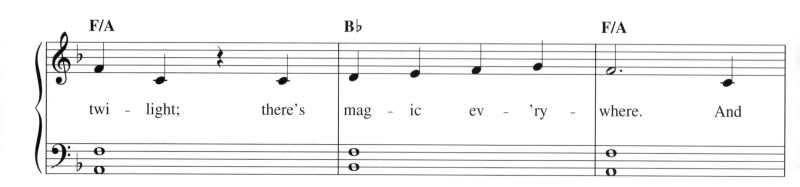

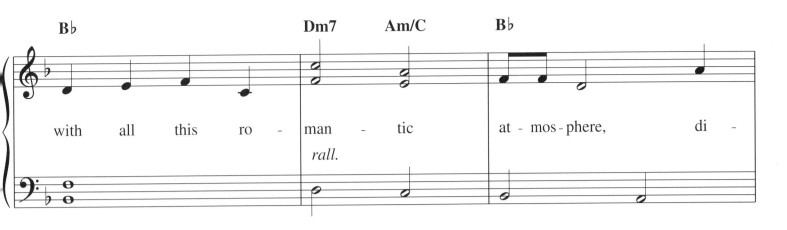

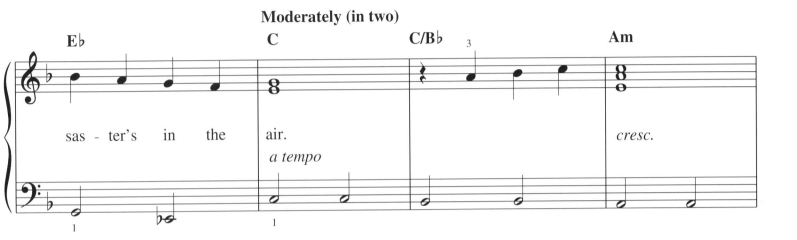

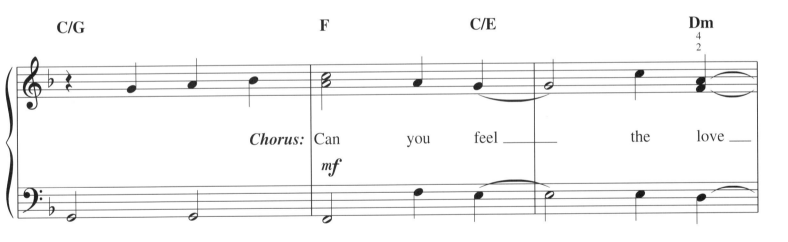

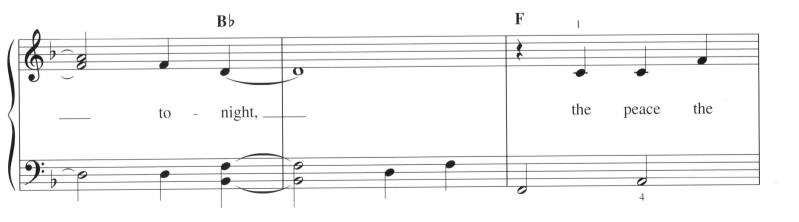

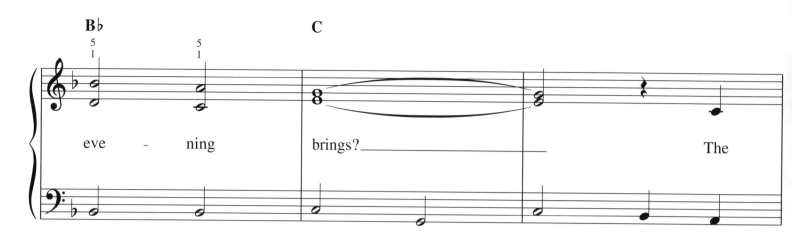

eve - ning   brings?_____   The

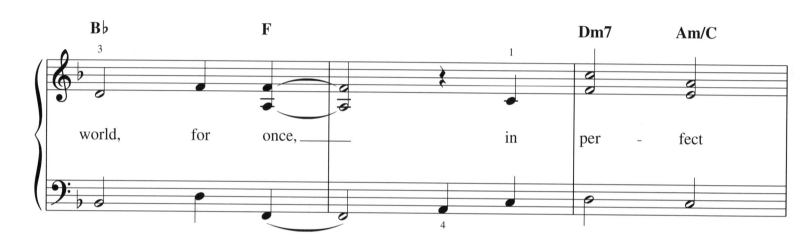

world,   for   once,_____   in   per - fect

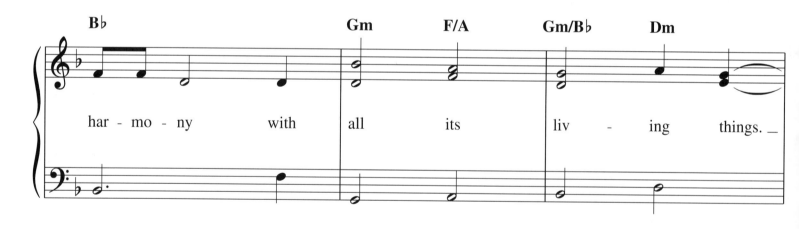

har - mo - ny   with   all   its   liv - ing   things. _

_____

dim.   *Simba:* So   man - y   things   to

mp

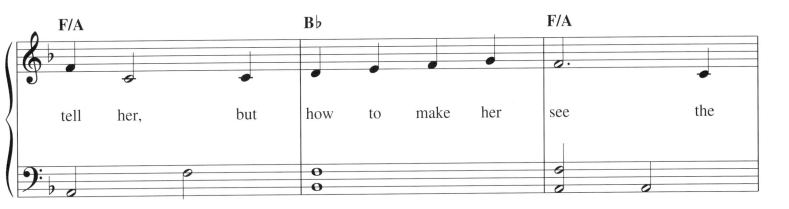

tell her,   but   how   to   make   her   see   the

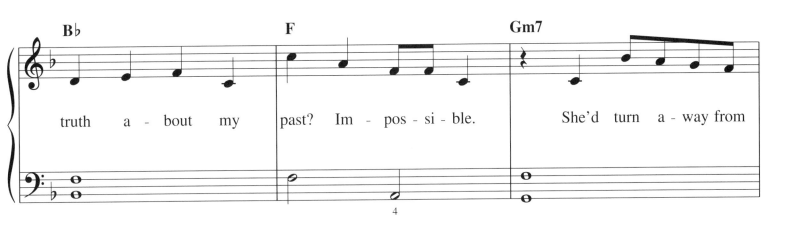

truth   a - bout   my   past? Im - pos - si - ble.   She'd turn a - way from

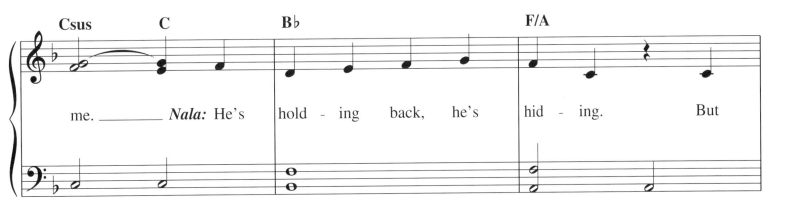

me. _____ *Nala:* He's   hold - ing   back,   he's   hid - ing.   But

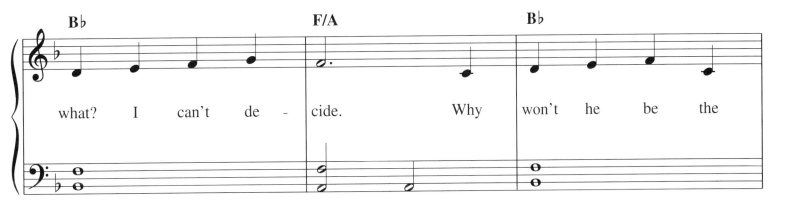

what?   I   can't   de - cide.   Why   won't   he   be   the

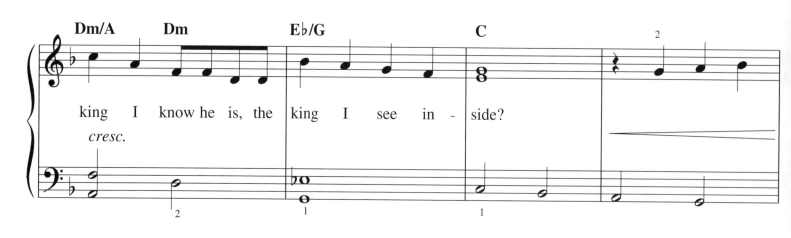

king I know he is, the king I see in - side?
cresc.

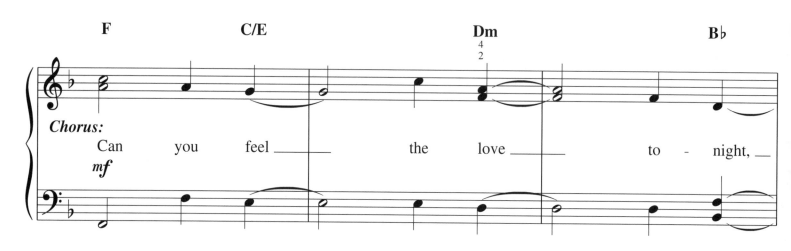

Chorus:
Can you feel the love to - night, __
mf

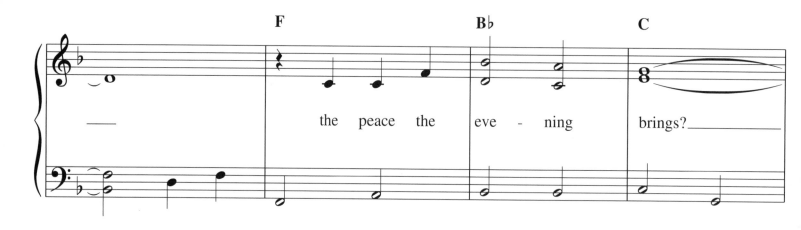

__ the peace the eve - ning brings? __

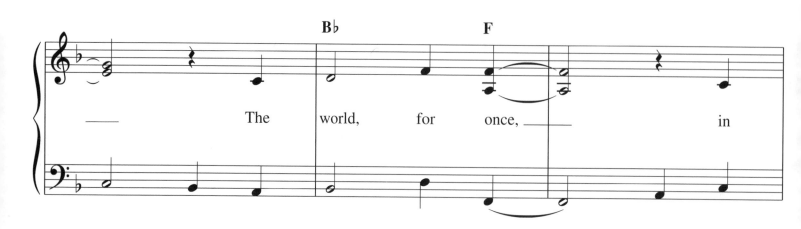

__ The world, for once, __ in

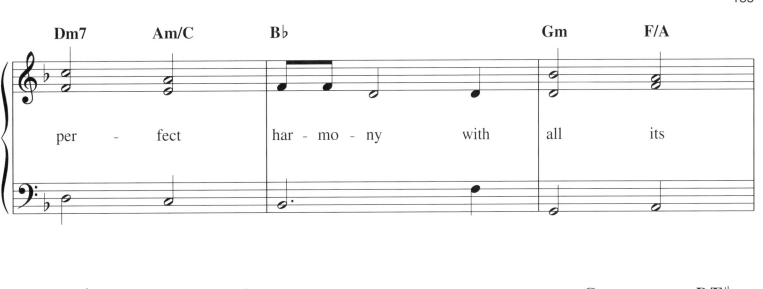

per - fect har - mo - ny with all its

liv - ing things. *cresc.* Can you feel ___ *f*

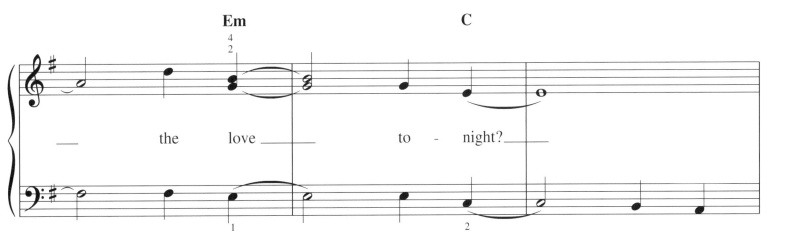

___ the love ___ to - night? ___

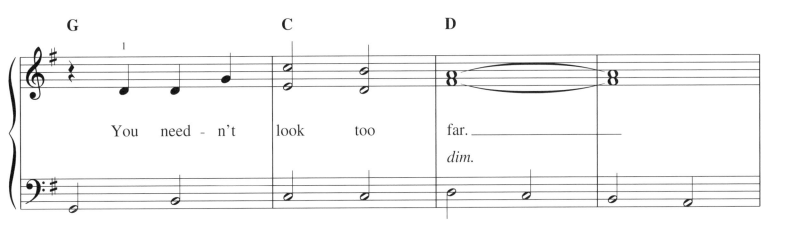

You need - n't look too far. ___ *dim.*

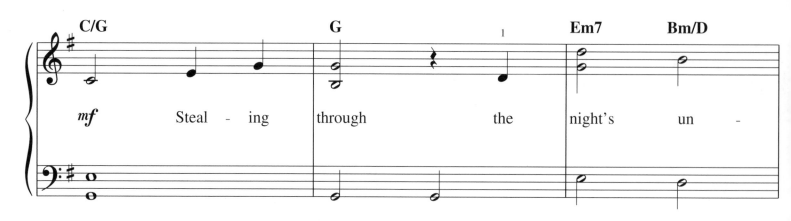

Steal - ing   through   the   night's   un -

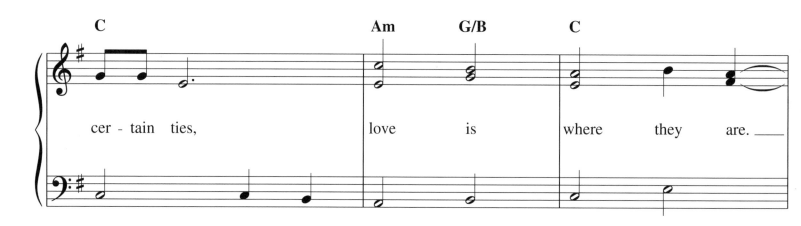

cer - tain   ties,   love   is   where   they   are. ____

____   *Timon:* And   if   he

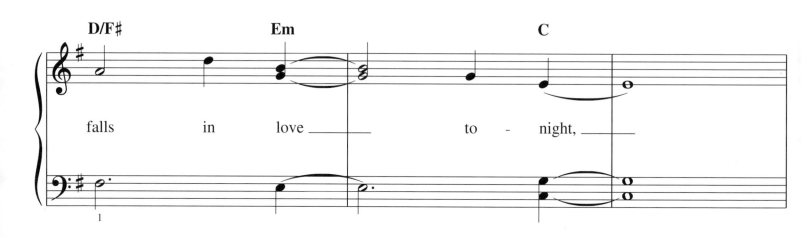

falls   in   love ____   to - night, ____

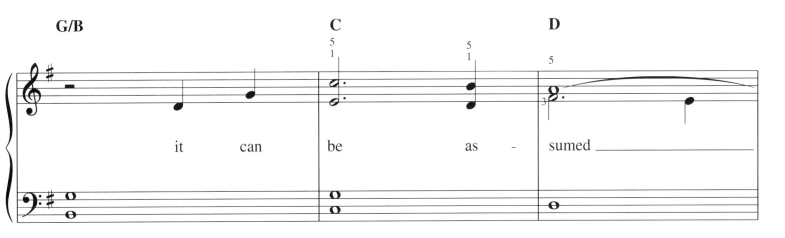

G/B   **C**   **D**

it can   be   as - sumed _____

C   **G/B**

___   *Pumbaa:* his care - free days   with

Em7   **Bm/D**   **C**   **Am**   **G/B**

us   are   his - tory,   in   short,   our

Timon And Pumbaa:

rall.

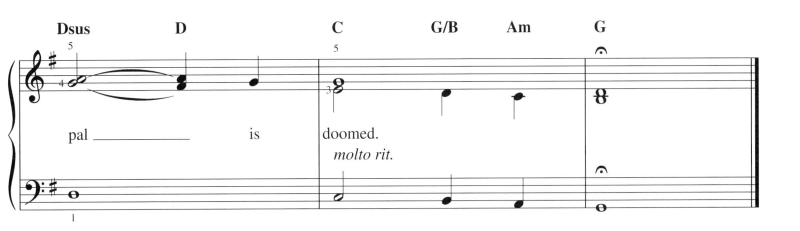

Dsus   **D**   **C**   **G/B**   **Am**   **G**

pal _____ is   doomed.

molto rit.

CIRCLE OF LIFE

from Walt Disney Pictures' THE LION KING

Music by ELTON JOHN
Lyrics by TIM RICE

Moderately

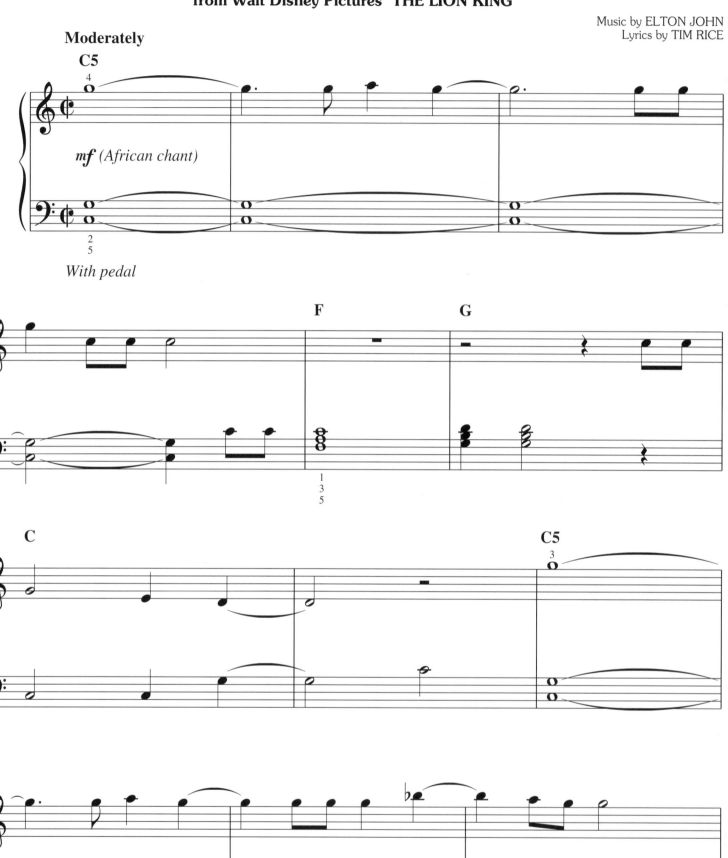

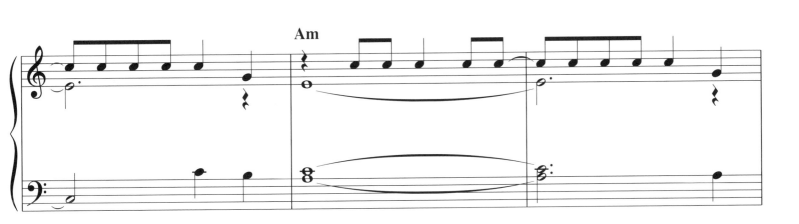

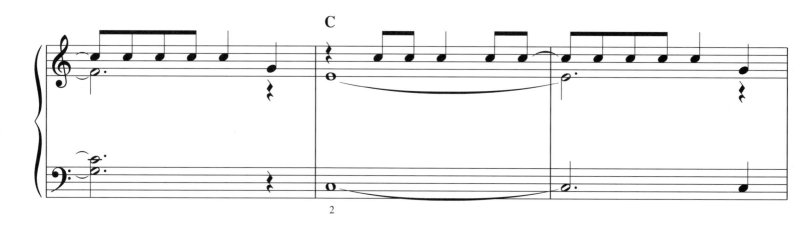

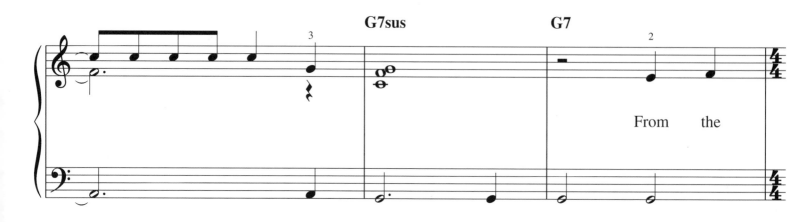

From the

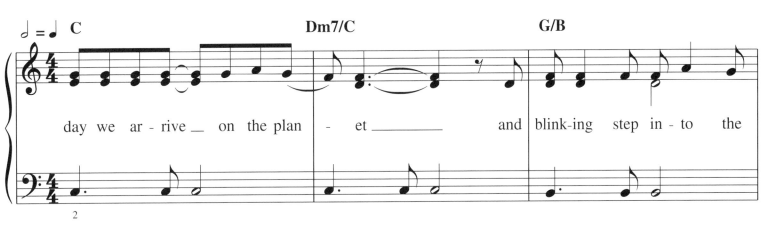

day we ar - rive ___ on the plan - et _____ and blink-ing step in - to the

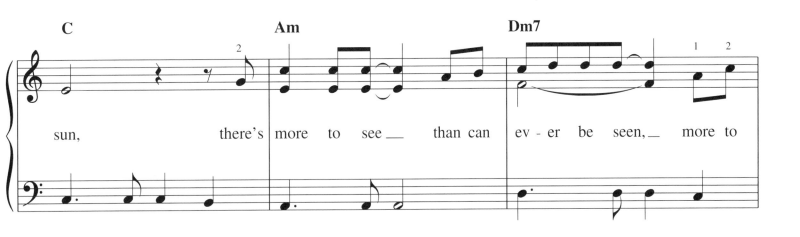

sun, there's more to see ___ than can ev - er be seen, ___ more to

do than can ev - er be done. _____ There's far too much ___ to take

in here, more to find than can ev - er be found. But the

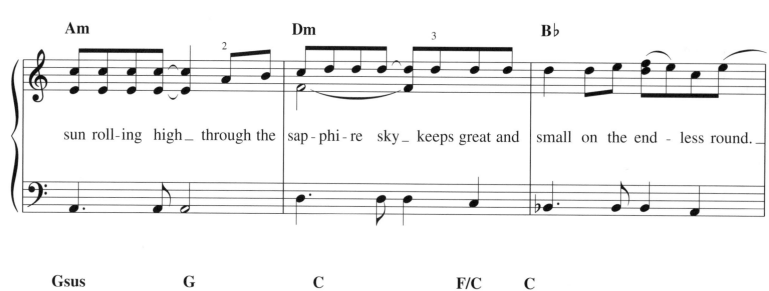

sun roll-ing high_ through the sap-phi-re sky_ keeps great and small on the end - less round.

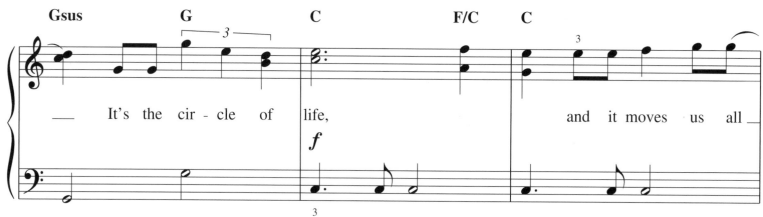

_ It's the cir - cle of life, and it moves us all_

_ through de - spair and hope, _____

through faith and _ love, 'til we find our

HAKUNA MATATA

from Walt Disney Pictures' THE LION KING

Music by ELTON JOHN
Lyrics by TIM RICE

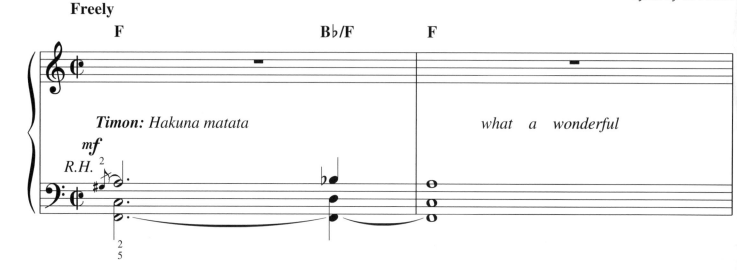

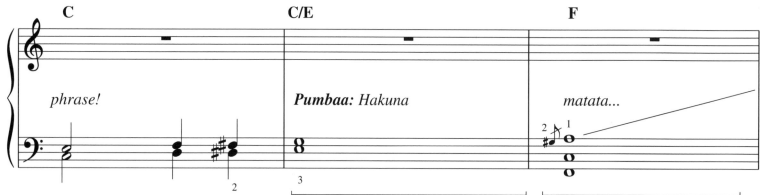

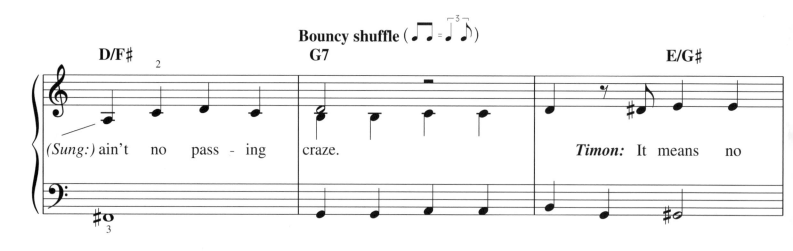

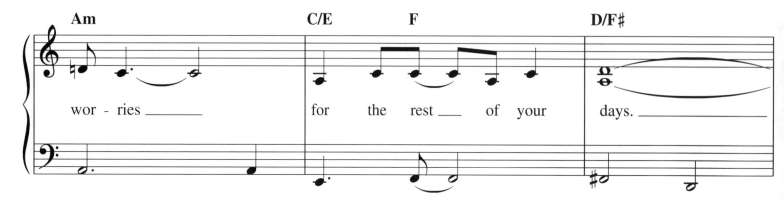

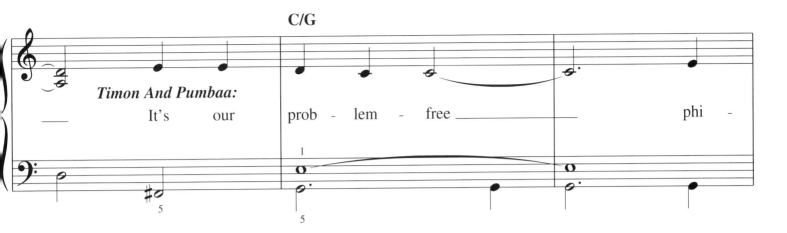

C/G

Timon And Pumbaa: It's our prob - lem - free _____ phi -

G **C**

lo - so - phy. ___ *Timon:* Ha - ku - na ma - ta - ta. ___

rall.

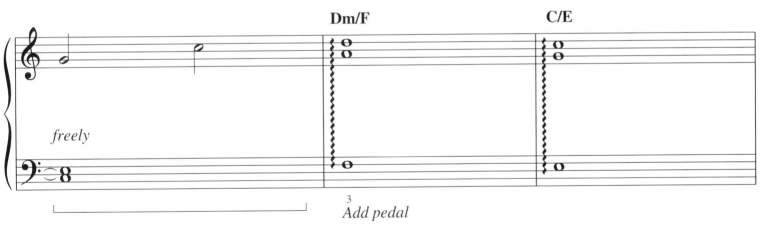

Dm/F **C/E**

freely

³ *Add pedal*

G **Dm** **Am**

198

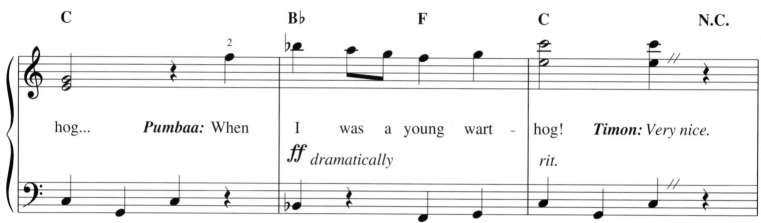

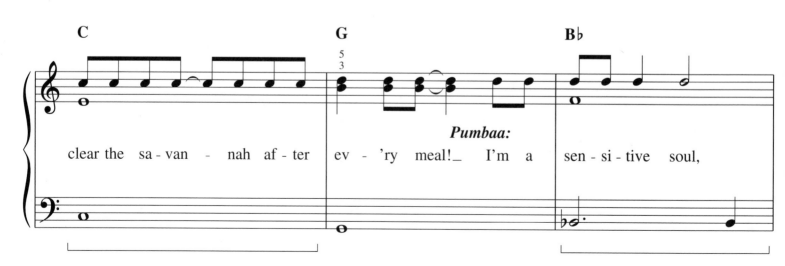

199

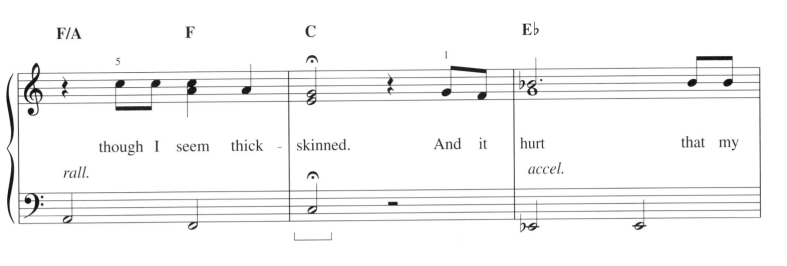

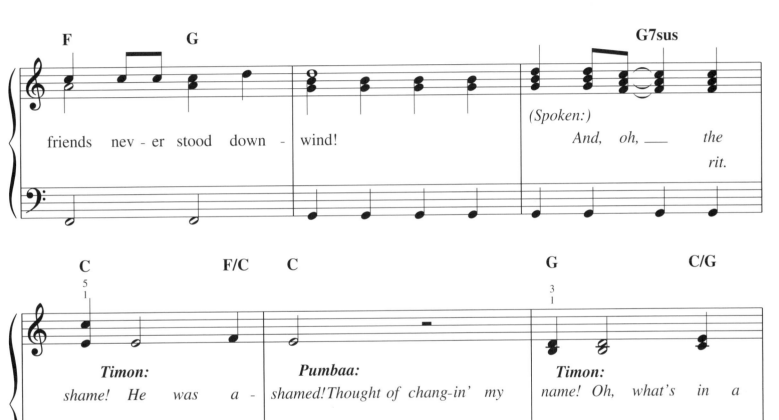

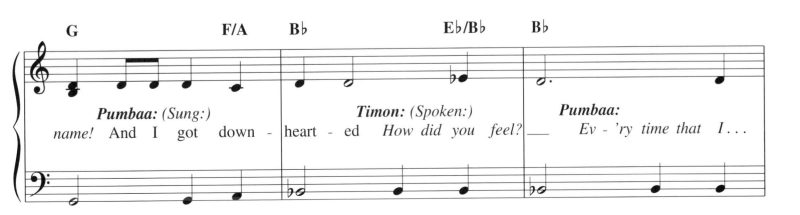

Timon:
Hey, Pumbaa, not in front *of the kids.* *Oh, sorry.*

Timon Ana Pumbaa:

a tempo

Ha - ku - na ma -

ta - ta... _____ what a won - der - ful phrase.

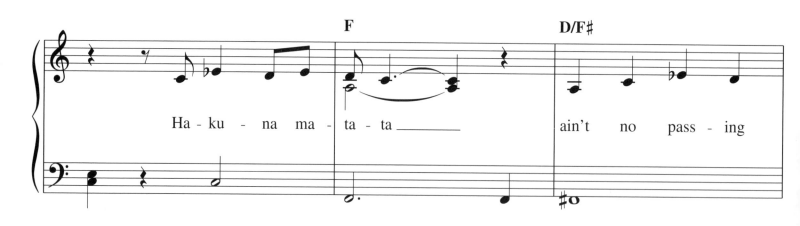

Ha - ku - na ma - ta - ta _____ ain't no pass - ing

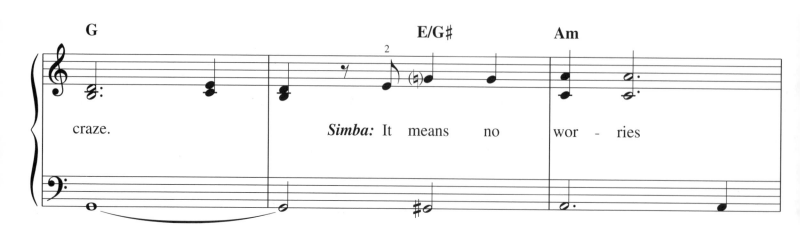

craze. **Simba:** It means no wor - ries

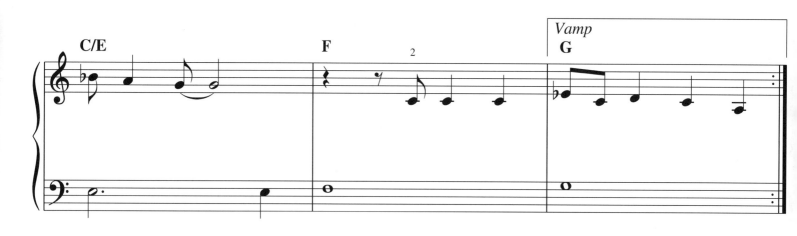

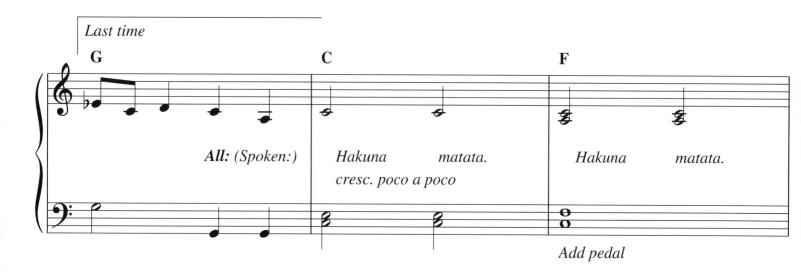

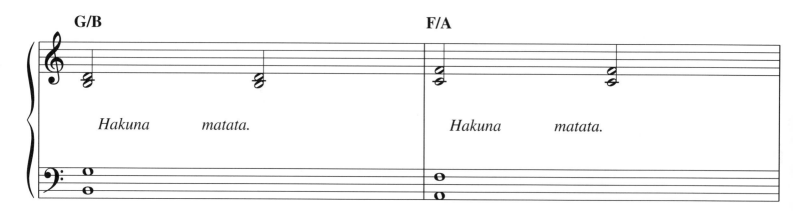

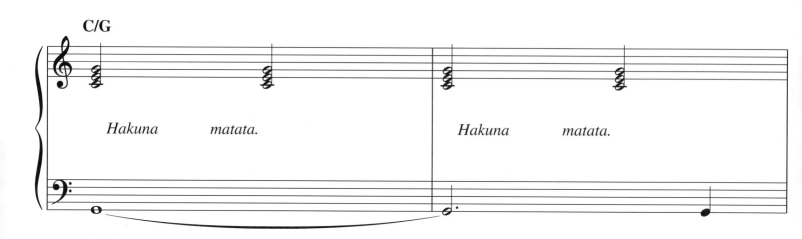

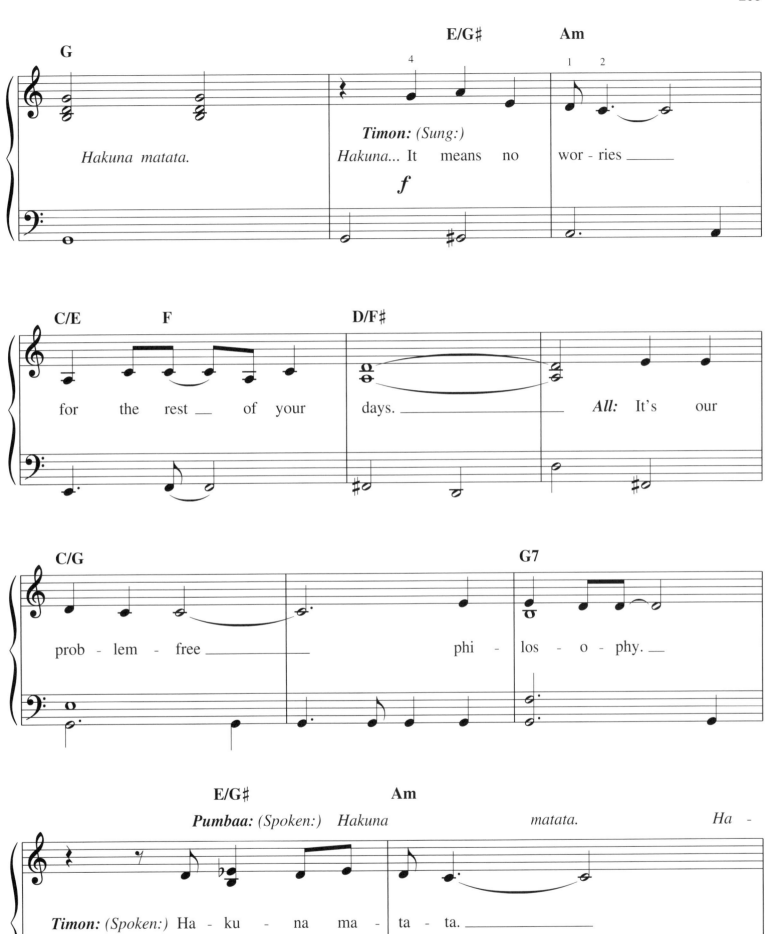

I JUST CAN'T WAIT TO BE KING

from Walt Disney Pictures' THE LION KING

Music by ELTON JOHN
Lyrics by TIM RICE

Simba: I'm gon-na be a might-y king, so

206

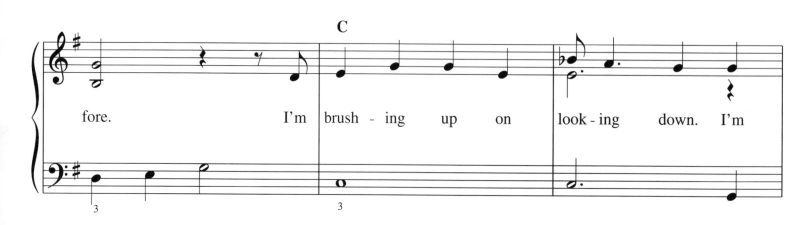

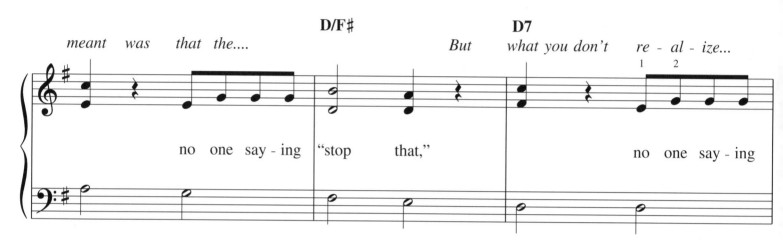

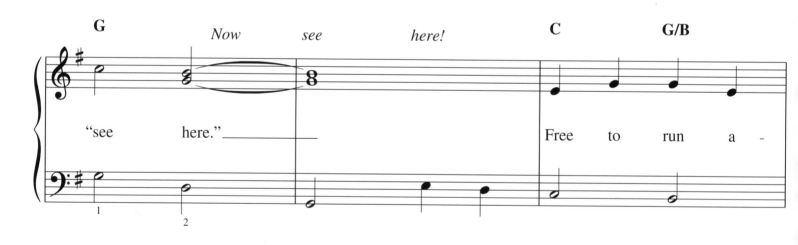

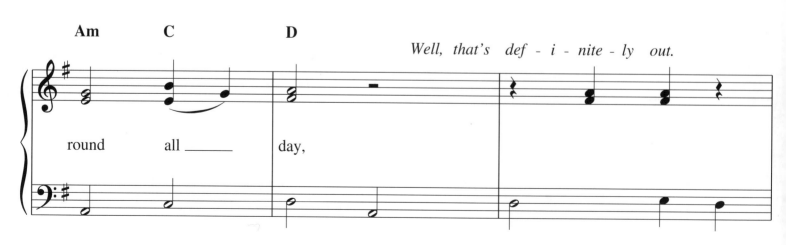

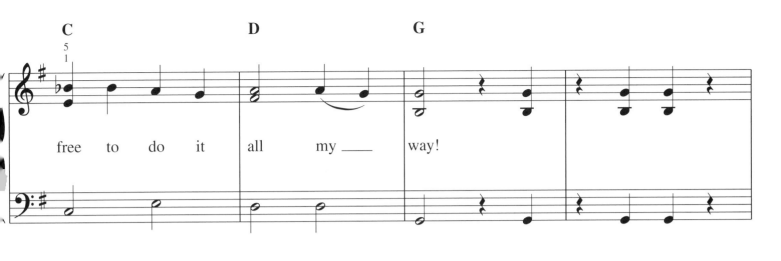

free to do it all my ___ way!

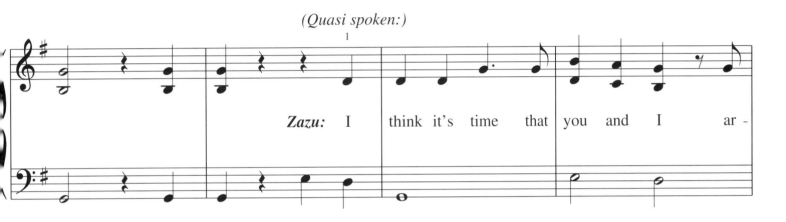

(Quasi spoken:)

Zazu: I think it's time that you and I ar -

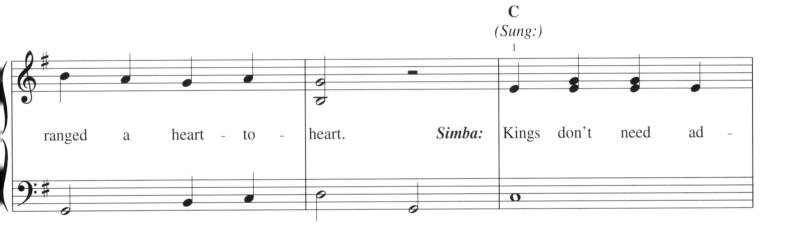

(Sung:)

ranged a heart - to - heart. ***Simba:*** Kings don't need ad -

(Quasi spoken:)

vice from lit - tle horn - bills, for a start. ***Zazu:*** If

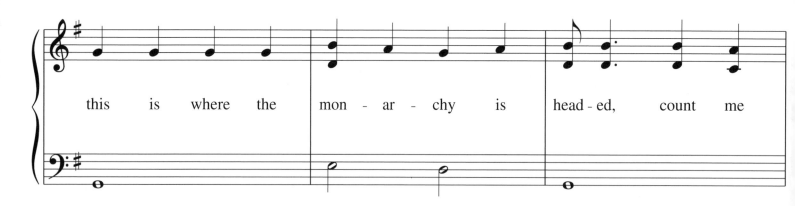

this is where the mon - ar - chy is head - ed, count me

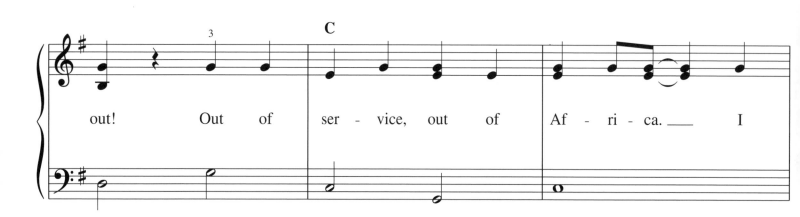

out! Out of ser - vice, out of Af - ri - ca. ___ I

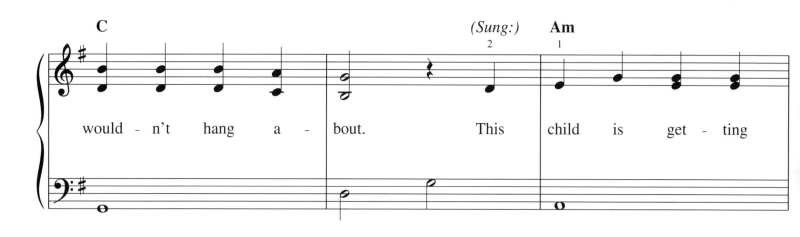

would - n't hang a - bout. This child is get - ting

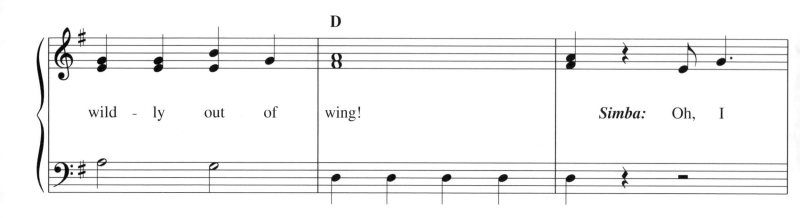

wild - ly out of wing! **Simba:** Oh, I

just   can't ____   wait   to   be   king!

Simba: Ev-'ry-bod-y   look   left,

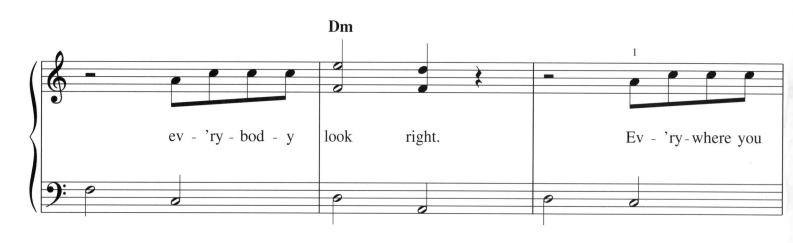

ev - 'ry - bod - y   look   right.   Ev - 'ry-where you

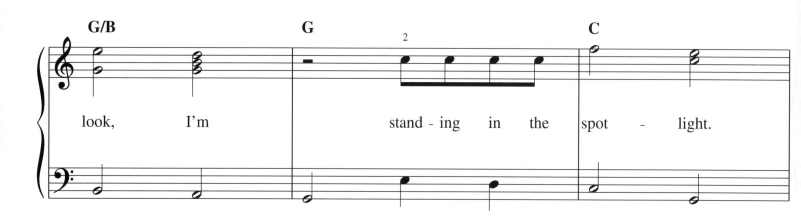

look,   I'm   stand - ing   in the   spot - light.

Zazu: (Spoken:)

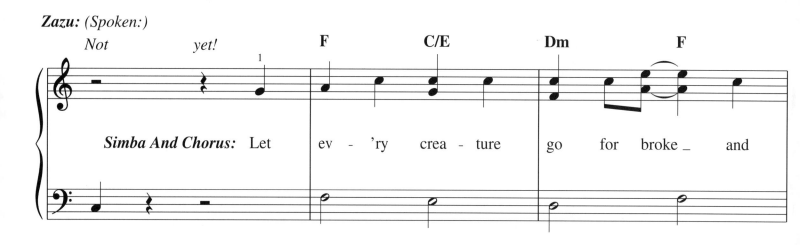

Not   yet!   **Simba And Chorus:** Let   ev - 'ry   crea - ture   go   for broke _   and

sing. _____   Let's   hear   it   in the

herd and on _____ the wing. _____ It's

gon - na be King Sim - ba's fin - est fling.

Simba: Oh, I just can't _____ wait to be

king.   Oh, I just can't _____

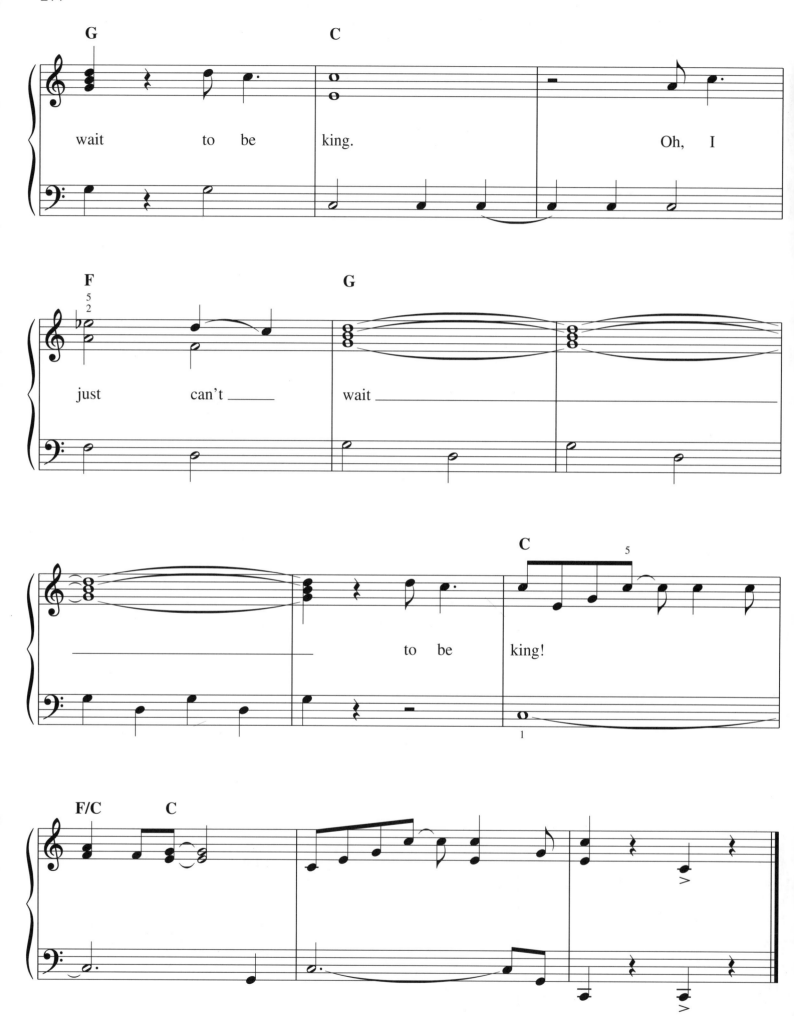

KISS THE GIRL
from Walt Disney's THE LITTLE MERMAID

Lyrics by HOWARD ASHMAN
Music by ALAN MENKEN

There   you   see   her

sit-ting there a-cross the   way   She don't got a lot to say,

but there's some - thing a - bout her. And you

don't know why, __ but you're dy - ing to try. You wan-na kiss the girl.

Yes, you want her.

Look at her, you know you do. Pos - si -ble she wants you, too. __

ain't that sad.__ Ain't it a shame, too bad.__ He gon-na miss the girl.__

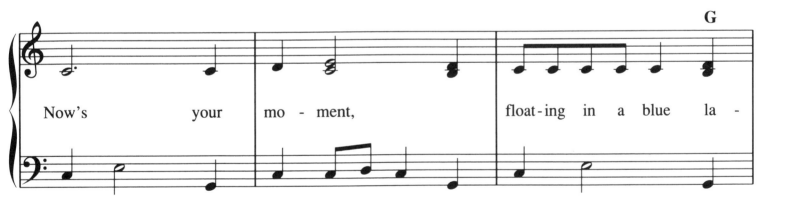

Now's your mo - ment, float-ing in a blue la -

goon. Boy, you bet -ter do it soon, no time will be

LES POISSONS
from Walt Disney's THE LITTLE MERMAID

Lyrics by HOWARD ASHMAN
Music by ALAN MENKEN

Moderately

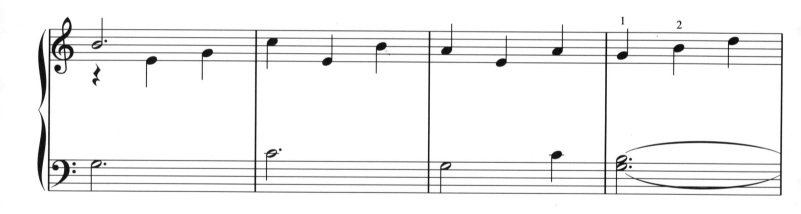

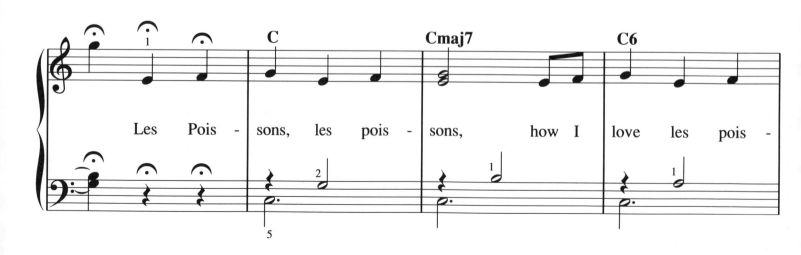

Les Pois - sons, les pois - sons, how I love les pois -

223

sons, love to chop and to serve lit - tle fish. ___

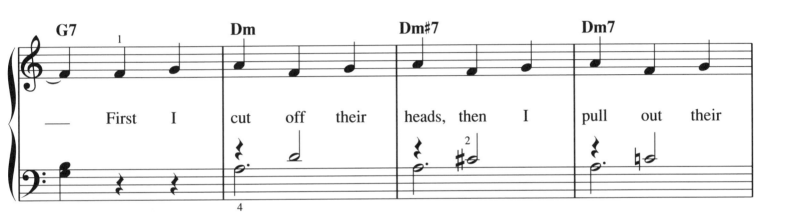

___ First I cut off their heads, then I pull out their

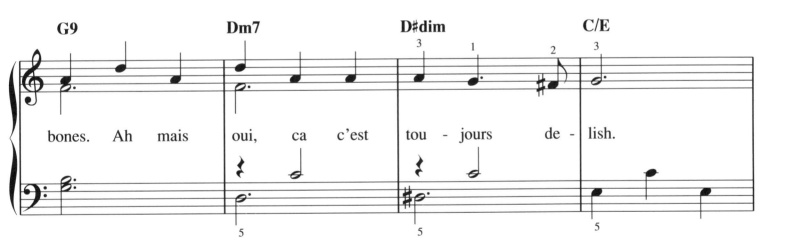

bones. Ah mais oui, ca c'est tou - jours de - lish.

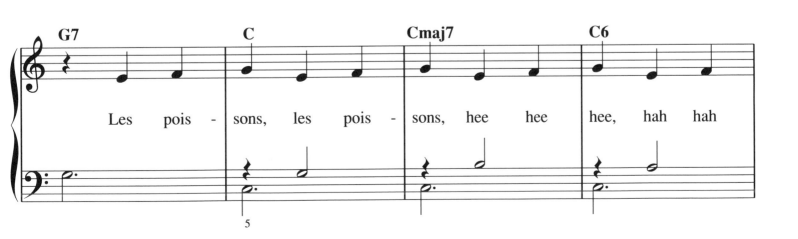

Les pois - sons, les pois - sons, hee hee hee, hah hah

hah. With the | clea - ver I | hack them in | two.

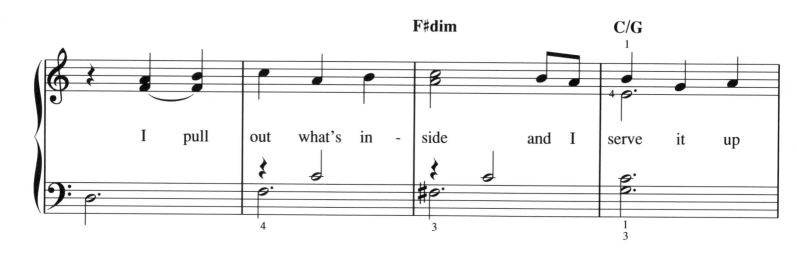

I pull | out what's in - side | and I | serve it up

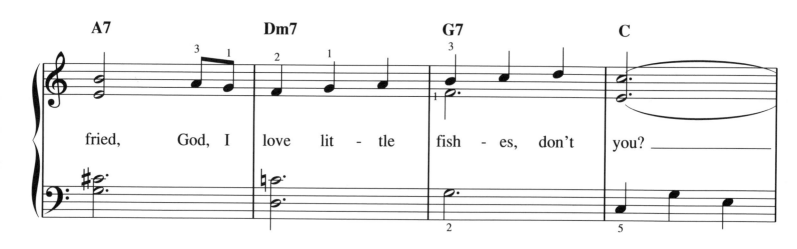

fried, | God, I love lit - tle | fish - es, don't | you? _____

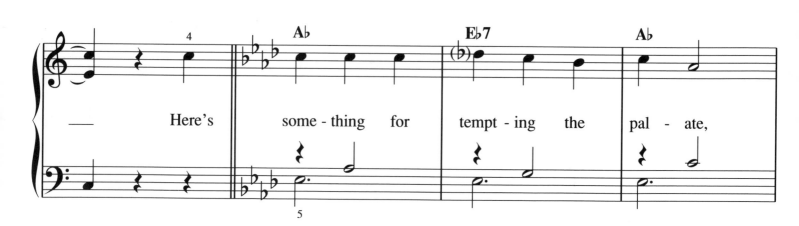

_____ Here's | some - thing for | tempt - ing the | pal - ate,

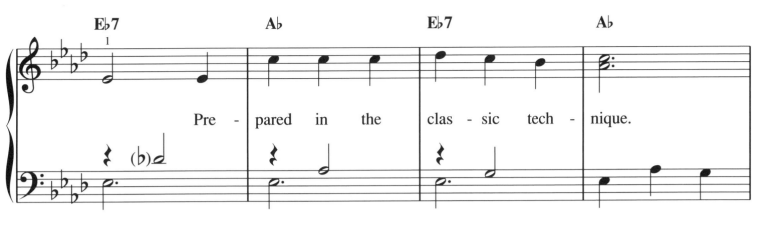

Pre - pared in the clas - sic tech - nique.

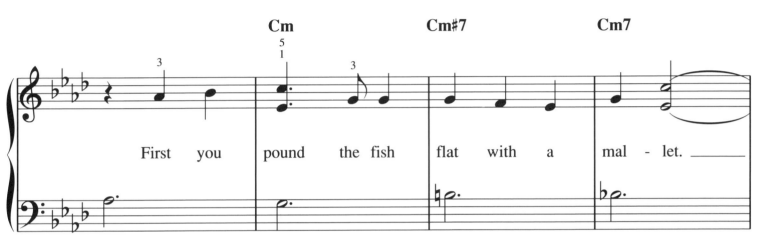

First you pound the fish flat with a mal - let. _____

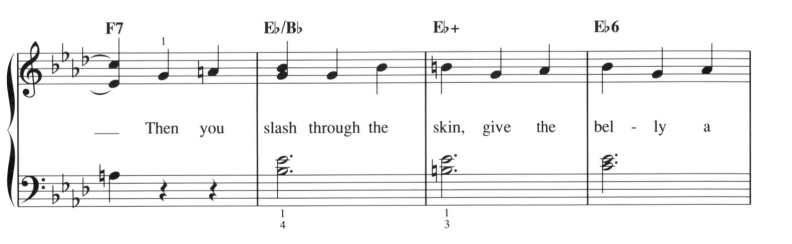

_____ Then you slash through the skin, give the bel - ly a

slice, then you rub some salt in 'cause that makes it taste

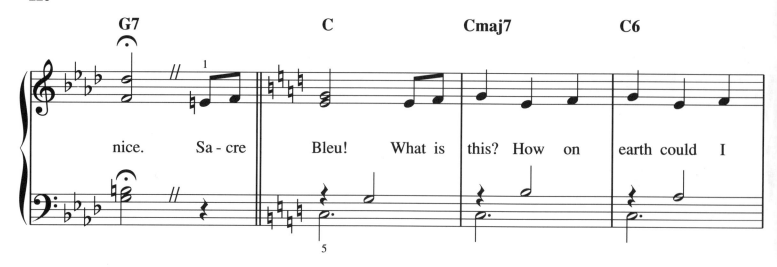

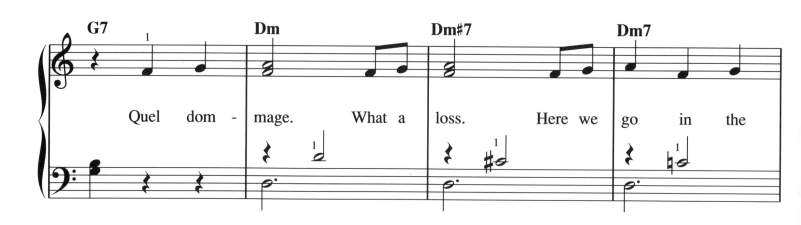

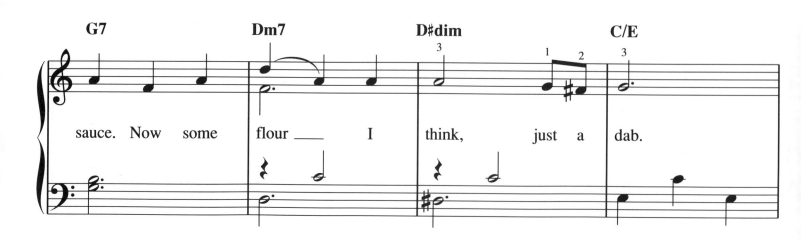

227

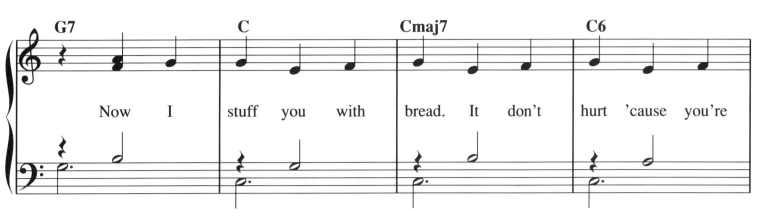

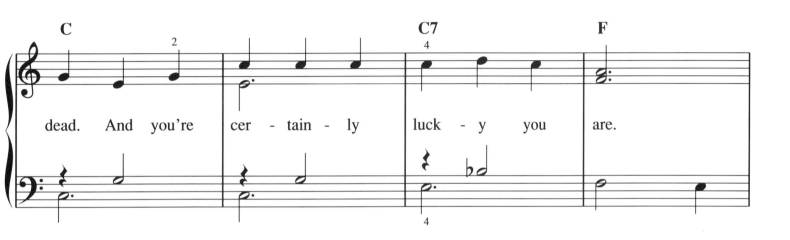

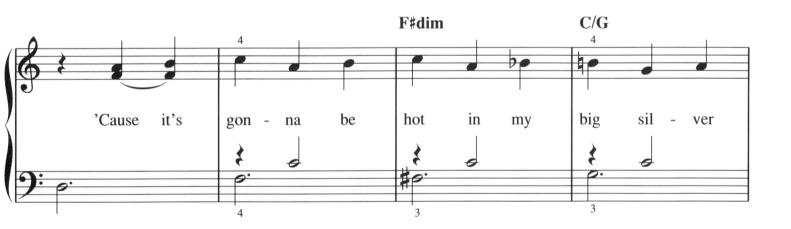

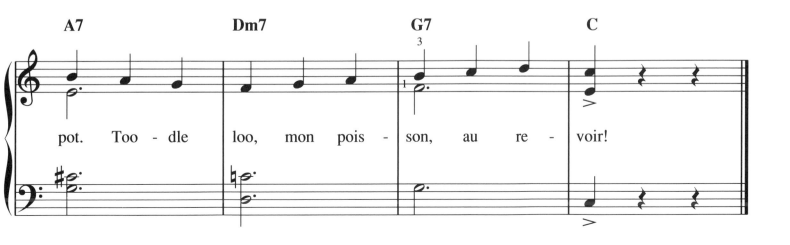

PART OF YOUR WORLD

from Walt Disney's THE LITTLE MERMAID

Lyrics by HOWARD ASHMAN
Music by ALAN MENKEN

229

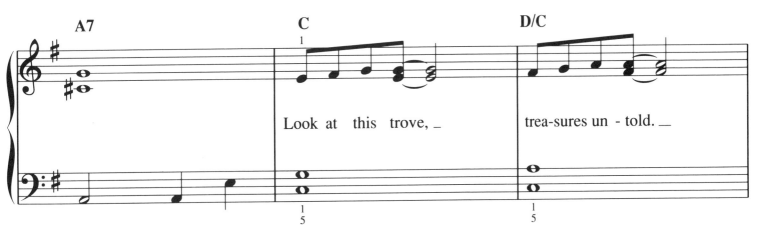

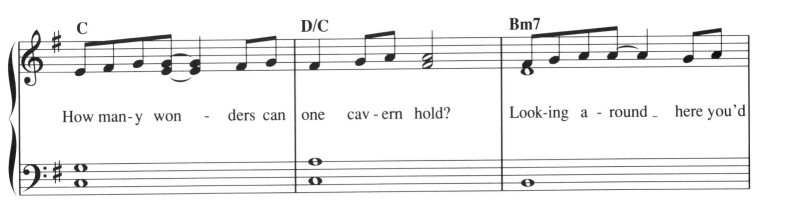

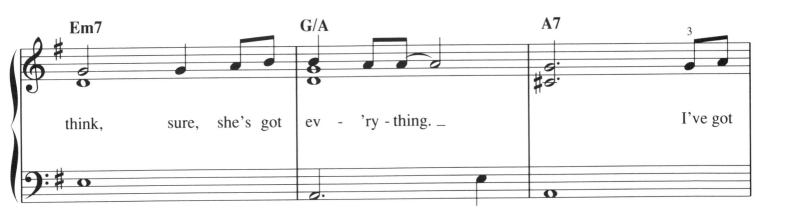

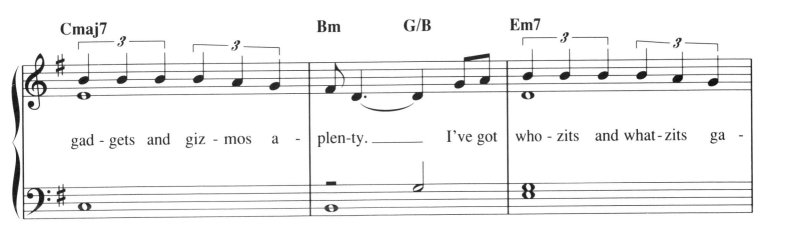

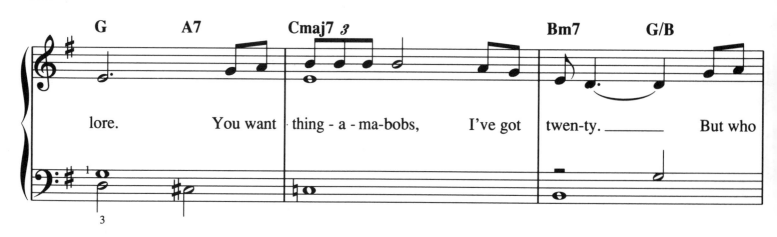

lore.   You want thing - a - ma-bobs, I've got twen-ty. _____ But who

cares?   No big deal.   I want more.

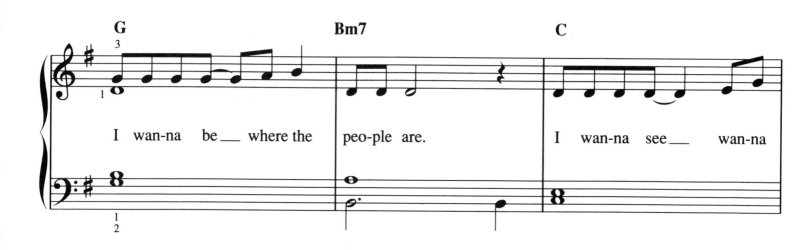

I wan-na be __ where the peo-ple are.   I wan-na see __ wan-na

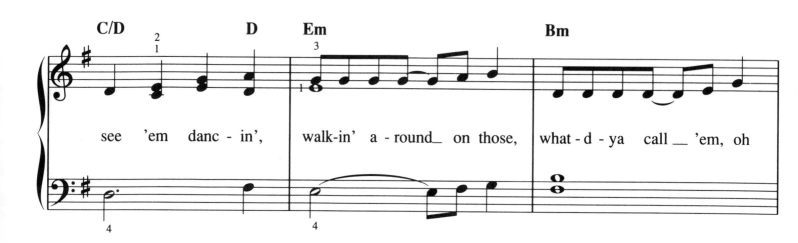

see 'em danc - in', walk-in' a - round __ on those, what-d - ya call __ 'em, oh

feet.   Flip-pin' your fins __ you don't

get   too   far.   Legs are re - quired __ for   jump - in', danc - in'.

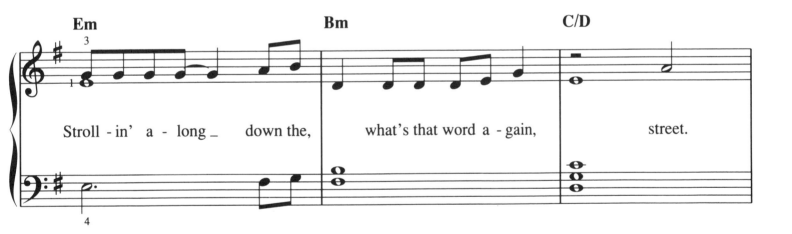

Stroll - in' a - long __ down the,   what's that word a - gain,   street.

Up where they   walk,   up where they   run,   up where they

stay all day in the sun. Wan - der - in' free, wish I could

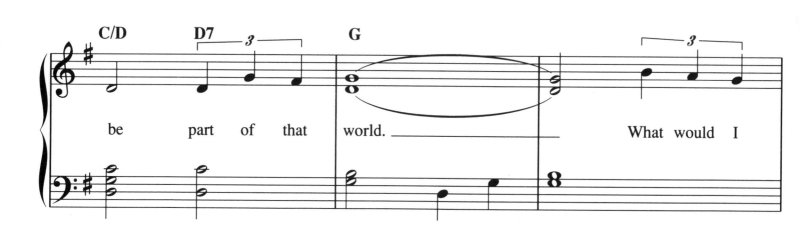

be part of that world. _____ What would I

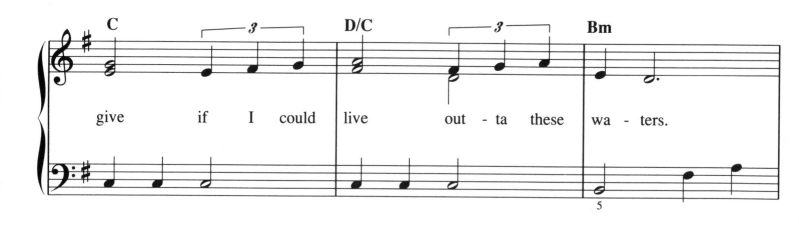

give if I could live out - ta these wa - ters.

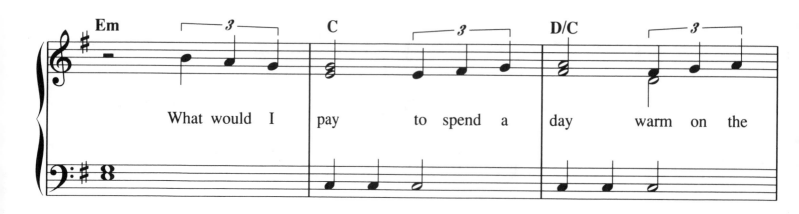

What would I pay to spend a day warm on the

sand.   Bet - cha on land they un - der -

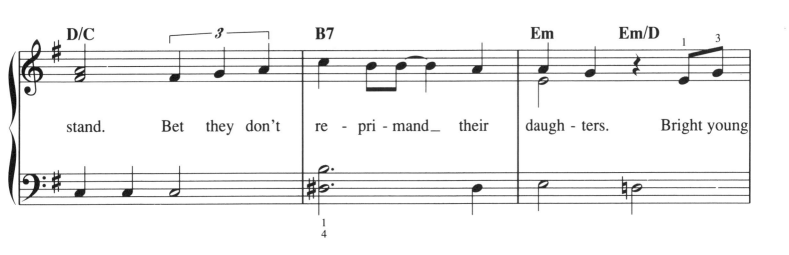

stand. Bet they don't re - pri - mand_ their daugh - ters. Bright young

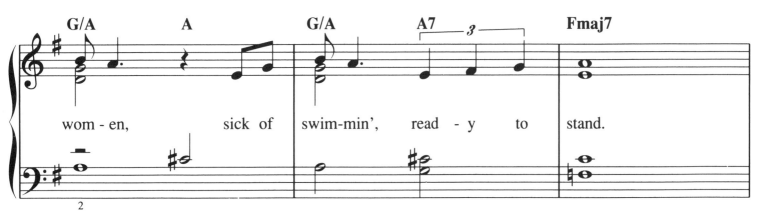

wom - en, sick of swim-min', read - y to stand.

And read - y to know_ what the peo - ple _ know.

Ask 'em my ques - tions and get some an - swers. What's a fire _____ and

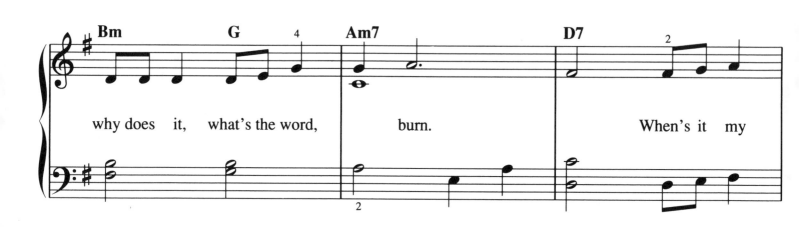

why does it, what's the word, burn. When's it my

turn? Would - n't I love, love to ex - plore that shore up a -

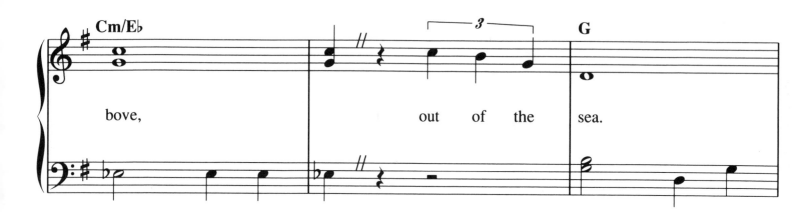

bove, out of the sea.

UNDER THE SEA
from Walt Disney's THE LITTLE MERMAID

Lyrics by HOWARD ASHMAN
Music by ALAN MENKEN

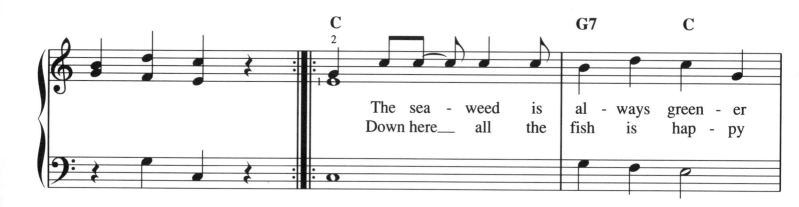

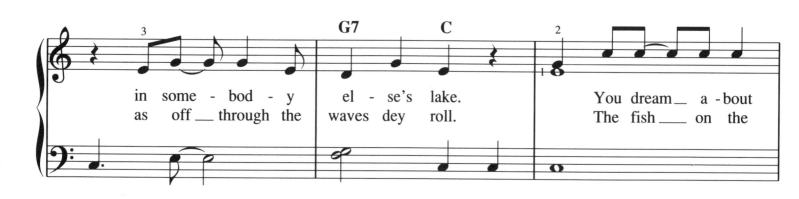

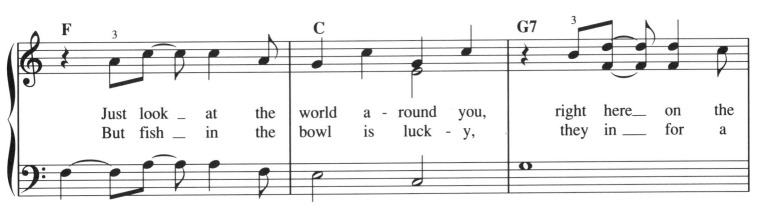

Just look _ at the world a - round you, right here_ on the
But fish _ in the bowl is luck - y, they in _ for a

o - cean floor. Such won - der - ful things sur - round you.
wors - er fate. One day _ when the boss get hun - gry

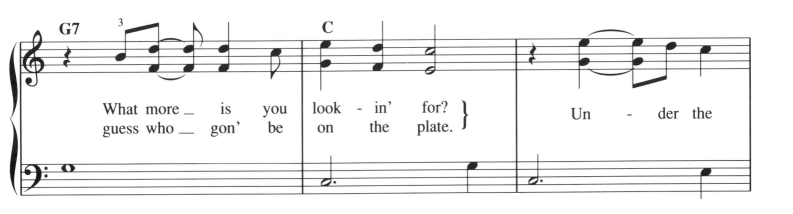

What more _ is you look - in' for? Un - der the
guess who _ gon' be on the plate.

sea, un - der the sea.

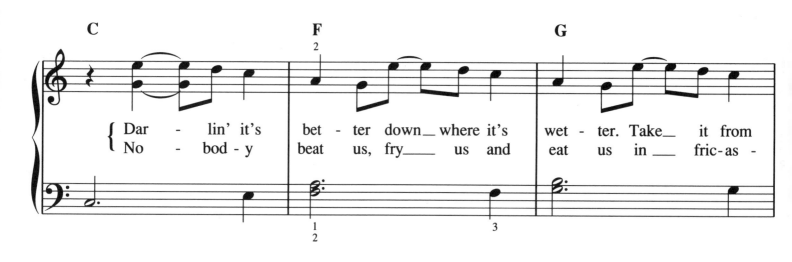

C   **F**   **G**

{ Dar - lin' it's   bet - ter down_ where it's   wet - ter. Take_ it from
No - bod - y   beat us, fry___ us and   eat us in _ fric-as -

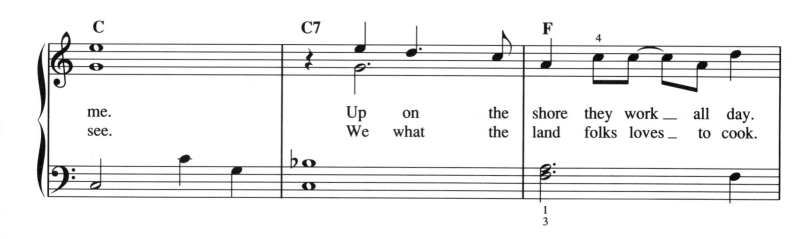

C   **C7**   **F**

me.   Up   on   the   shore they work _ all day.
see.   We   what   the   land folks loves _ to cook.

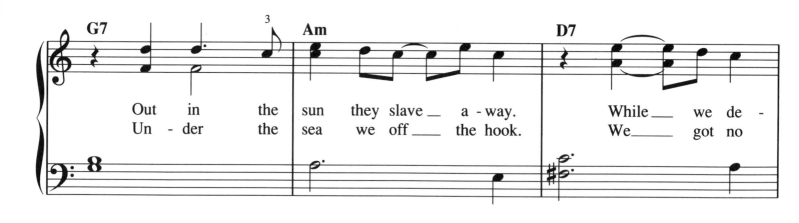

G7   **Am**   **D7**

Out   in   the   sun they slave _ a - way.   While_ we de -
Un - der   the   sea we off __ the hook.   We__ got no

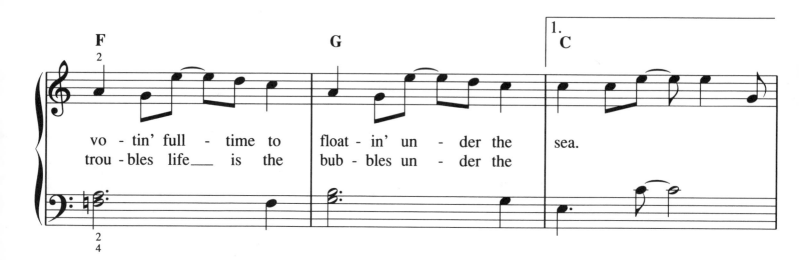

F   **G**   **1.** **C**

vo - tin' full - time to   float - in' un - der the   sea.
trou - bles life__ is the   bub - bles un - der the

239.

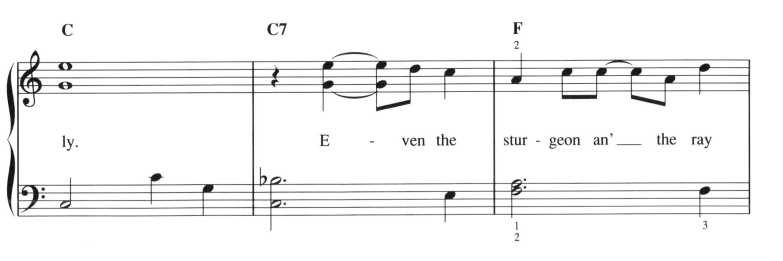

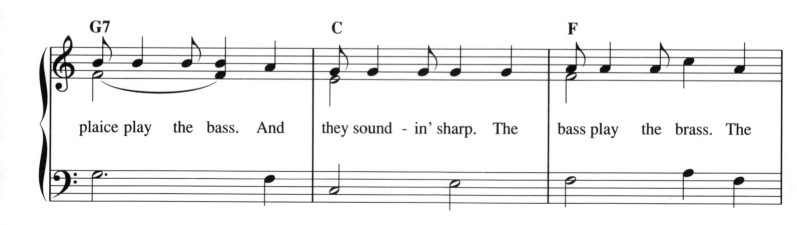

chub play the tub. The fluke is the duke of soul. The

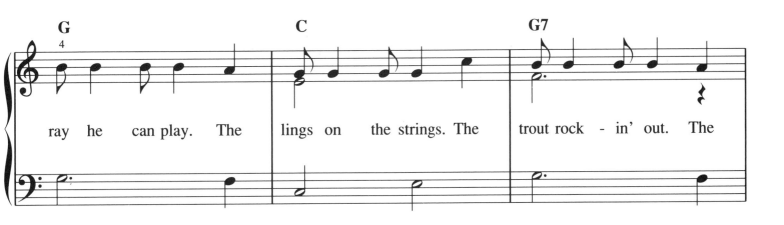

ray he can play. The lings on the strings. The trout rock - in' out. The

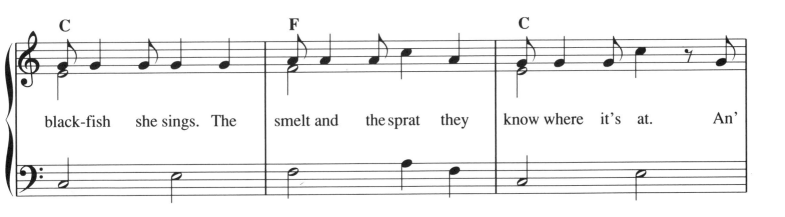

black-fish she sings. The smelt and the sprat they know where it's at. An'

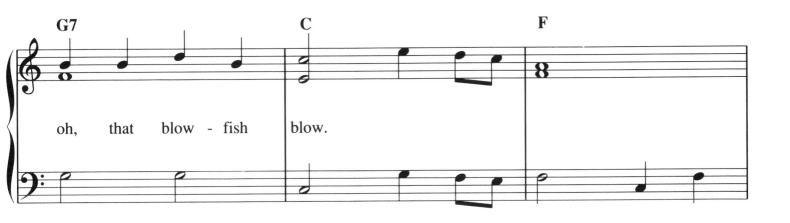

oh, that blow - fish blow.

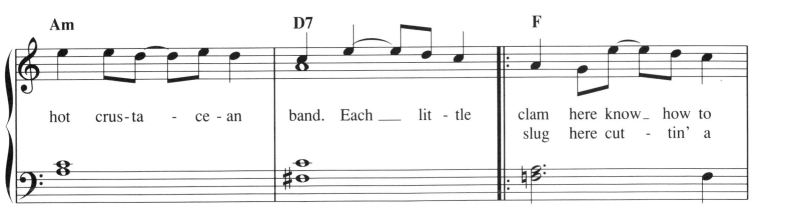

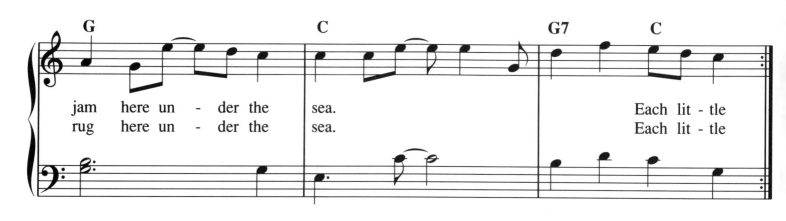

jam here un - der the sea.
rug here un - der the sea. Each lit - tle
Each lit - tle

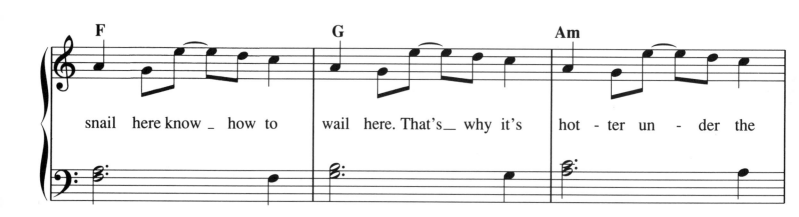

snail here know _ how to wail here. That's _ why it's hot - ter un - der the

wa - ter. Ya _ we in luck here down _ in the muck here un - der the

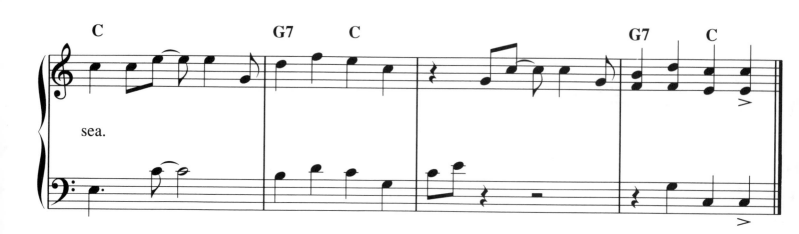

sea.

REFLECTION

(Pop Version)
from Walt Disney Pictures' MULAN

Music by MATTHEW WILDER
Lyrics by DAVID ZIPPEL

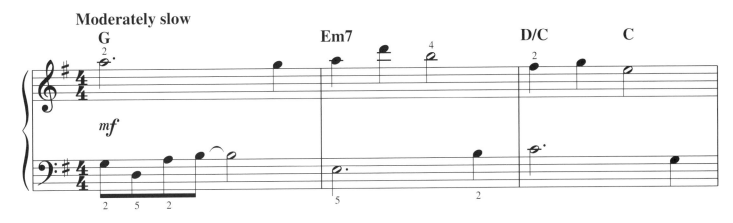

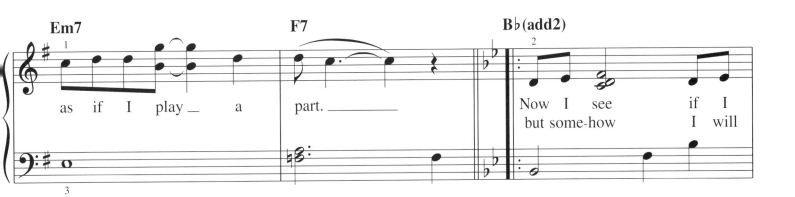

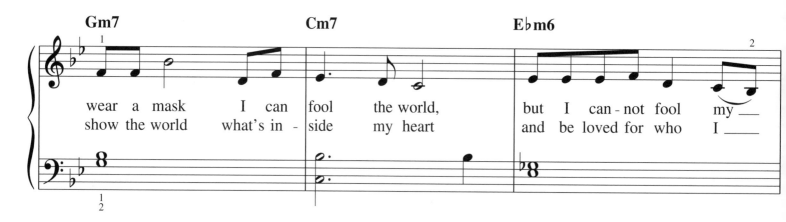

Gm7 / Cm7 / Ebm6

wear a mask   I can fool   the world,   but I can-not fool   my ___
show the world what's in - side   my heart   and be loved for who I ___

Bb

heart.
am.

Who   is that
Who   is that
Why   must we

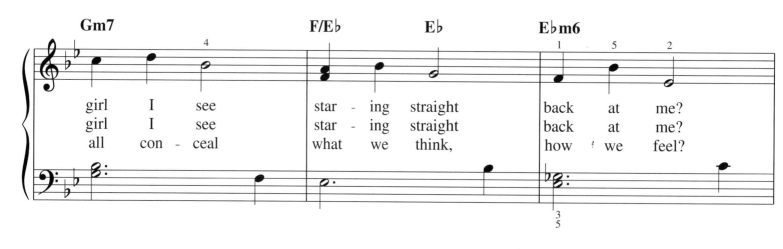

Gm7 / F/Eb Eb / Ebm6

girl   I   see   star - ing straight   back   at   me?
girl   I   see   star - ing straight   back   at   me?
all con - ceal   what we think,   how   we feel?

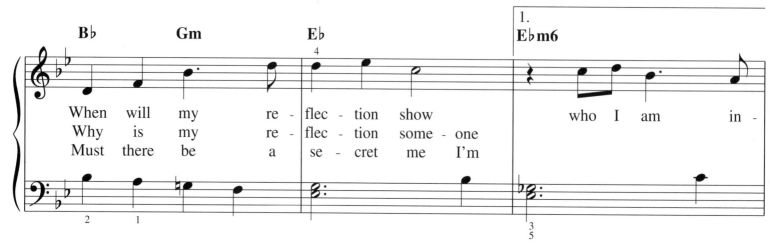

Bb   Gm / Eb / 1. Ebm6

When will my   re - flec - tion show   who I am   in-
Why   is   my   re - flec - tion some - one
Must there be   a   se - cret   me I'm

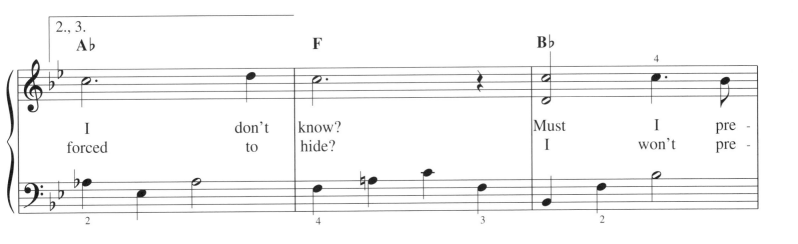

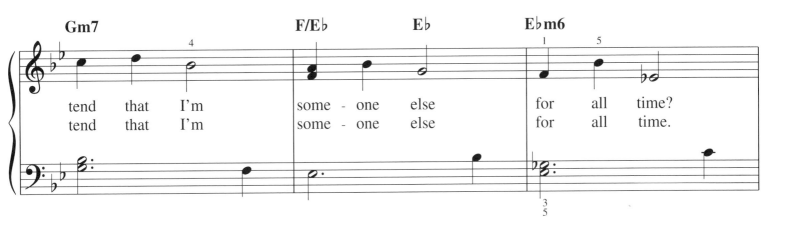

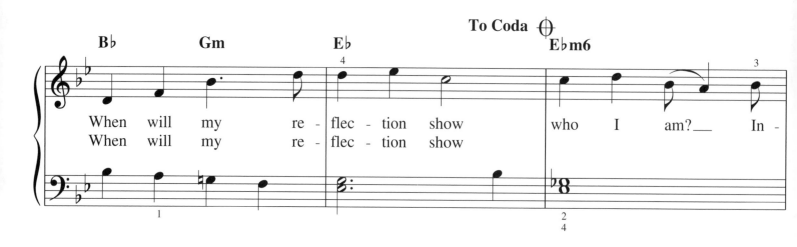

When will my re-flec-tion show who I am?__ In-
When will my re-flec-tion show

side, __ there's a heart that must be free to

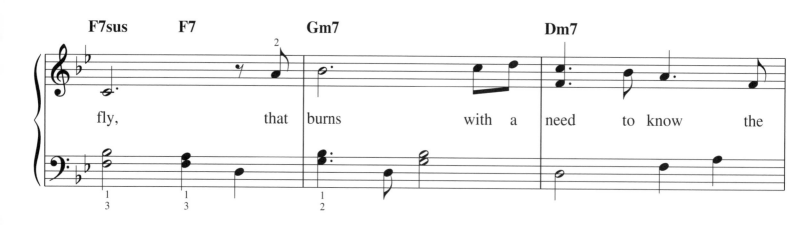

fly, that burns with a need to know the

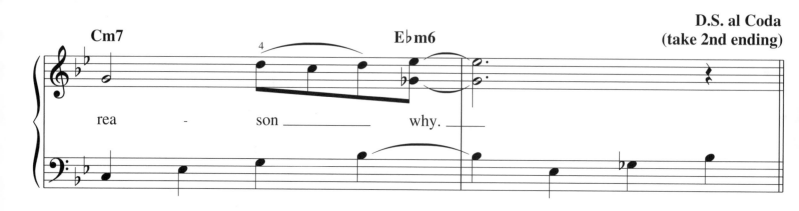

rea - son __ why. __

D.S. al Coda
(take 2nd ending)

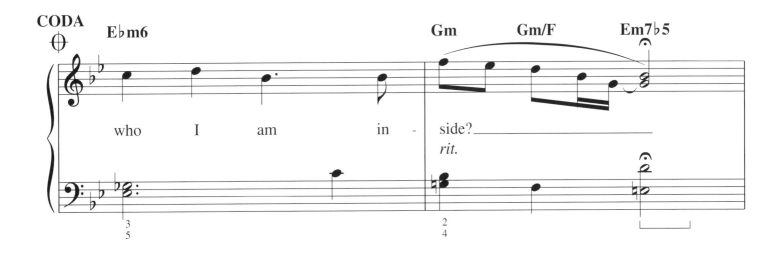

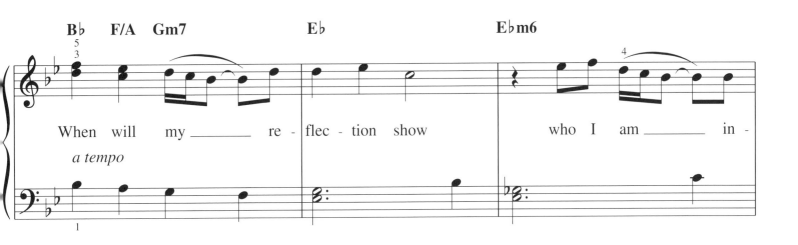

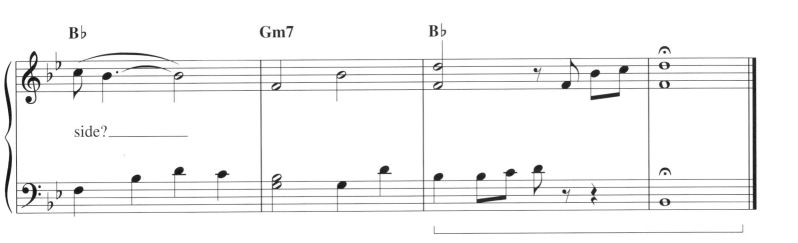

TRUE TO YOUR HEART

from Walt Disney Pictures' MULAN

Music by MATTHEW WILDER
Lyrics by DAVID ZIPPEL

tied to mine.
set you free.
I look in your eyes and see you search-ing
I can do that for you if you be -

F7

for a sign.
lieve in me.
But you'll nev - er fall
Why ___ sec - ond guess
'til what
what

G7

you let go. ___
feels so right? ___
Don't be so scared
Just trust your heart
of what
and you'll

C

you don't ___ know.
see the ___ light.
True to your heart, you must be

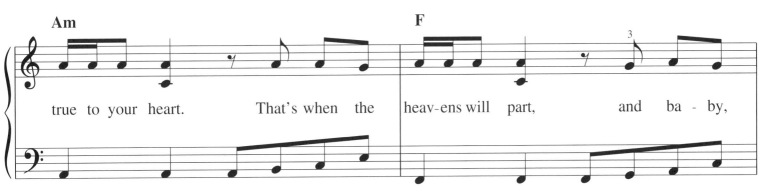

true to your heart.   That's when the   heav-ens will part,   and ba - by,

show - er   you   with   my   love.   O - pen your eyes,   your heart can

tell you no   lies.   And   when you're   true to your heart,   I   know   it's

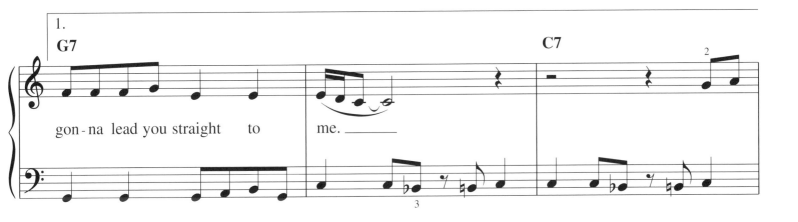

gon - na lead you straight   to   me. _____

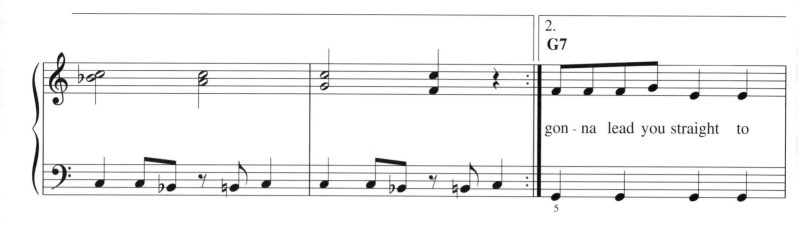

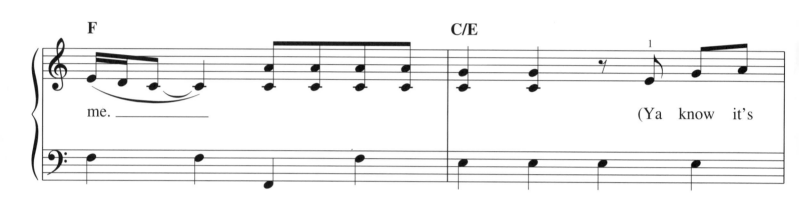

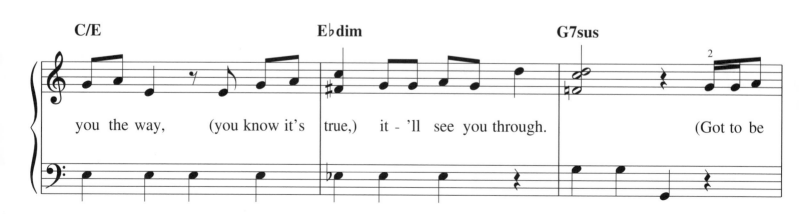

true)   (to your heart)

Girl, my heart is driv - ing me to

where you are;   you can take both hands off the wheel and

still get far.   Be _____ swept a - way,   en - joy the ride.   You

won't get lost   with your heart   to __ guide you.   True to your heart,   you must be

true to your heart.   That's when the   heav-ens will part,   and ba - by,

show - er   you   with   my   love.   O - pen your eyes,   your heart can

tell you no   lies.   And when you're   true to your heart,   I   know it's

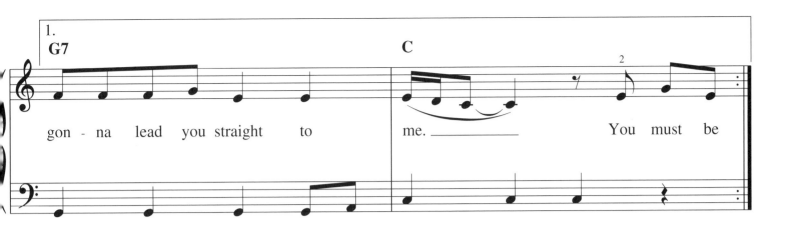

1.

G7 ... **C**

gon - na lead you straight to me. _____ You must be

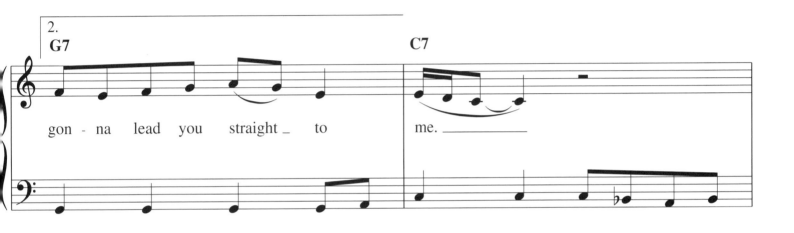

2.

G7 ... **C7**

gon - na lead you straight _ to me. _____

C7

When things are get - tin' cra - zy and you don't know where to start, ___
When all the world a - round you, it ___ seems to fall a - part, ___

258

keep on be - liev - ing, ba - by; just be true to your heart.
keep on be - liev - ing, ba - by; just be true to your heart.

Repeat and Fade

COLORS OF THE WIND
from Walt Disney Pictures' POCAHONTAS

Music by ALAN MENKEN
Lyrics by STEPHEN SCHWARTZ

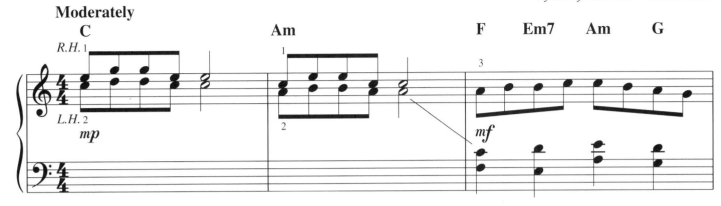

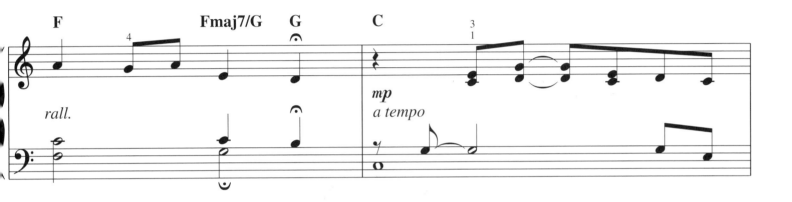

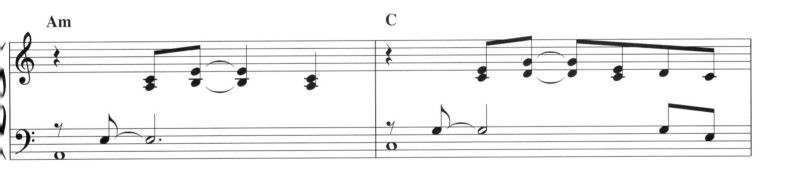

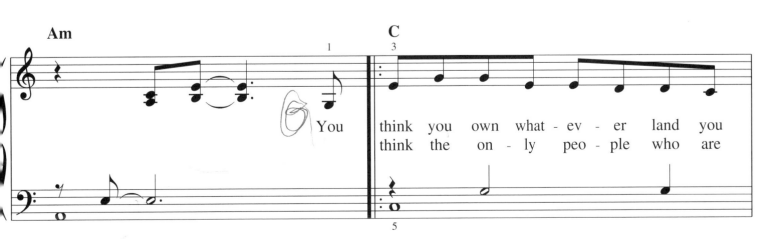

You think you own what-ev-er land you
think the on-ly peo-ple who are

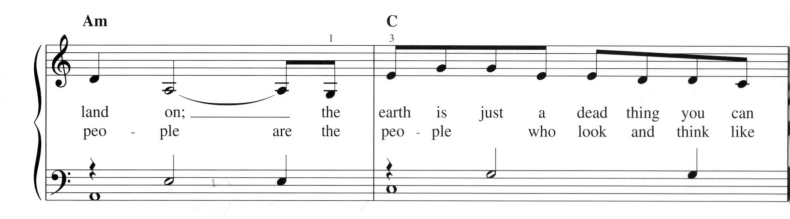

land   on; _____ the
peo - ple   are the

claim;   but
you,   but

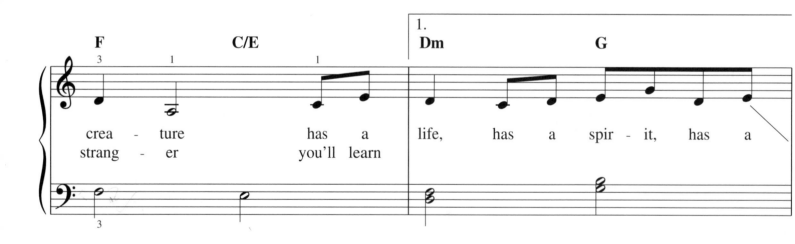

crea - ture   has a
strang - er   you'll learn

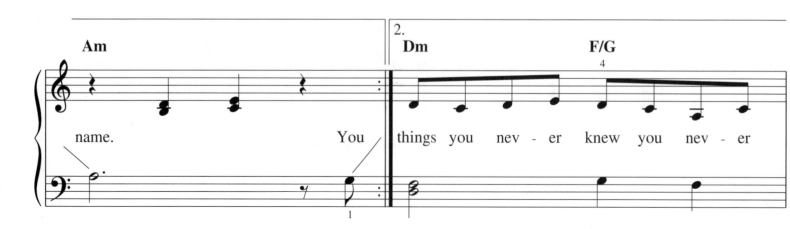

name.   You

knew. Have you ev - er heard the wolf cry to the

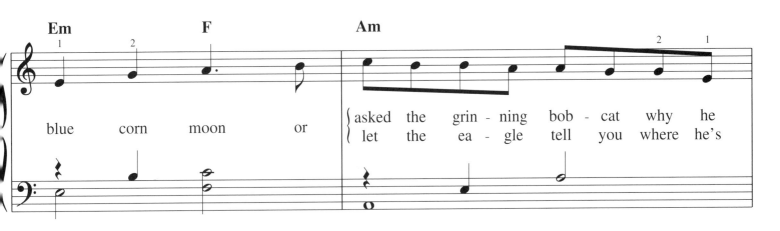

blue corn moon or asked the grin - ning bob - cat why he
let the ea - gle tell you where he's

grinned?
been? Can you sing with all the voic - es of the

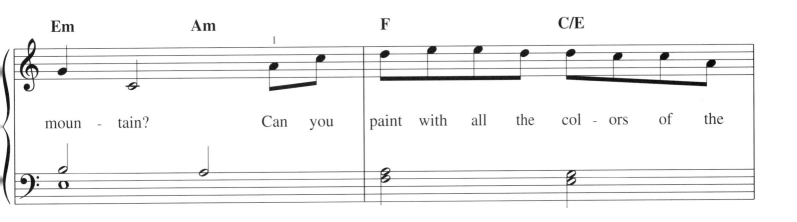

moun - tain? Can you paint with all the col - ors of the

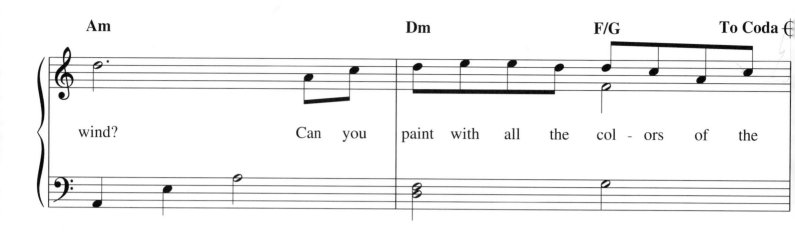

wind?   Can you   paint with   all   the   col - ors   of   the

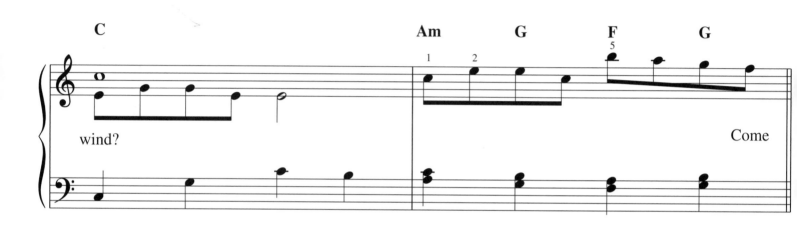

wind?   Come

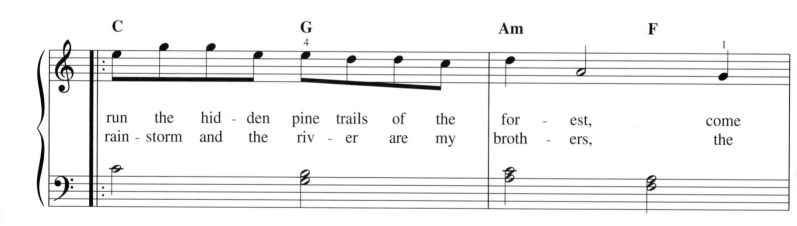

run   the   hid - den   pine   trails   of   the   for - est,   come
rain - storm   and   the   riv - er   are   my   broth - ers,   the

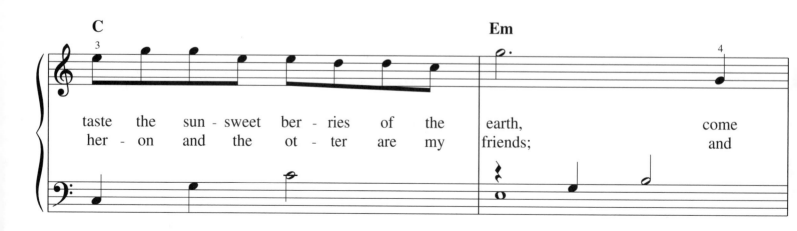

taste   the   sun - sweet   ber - ries   of   the   earth,   come
her - on   and   the   ot - ter   are   my   friends;   and

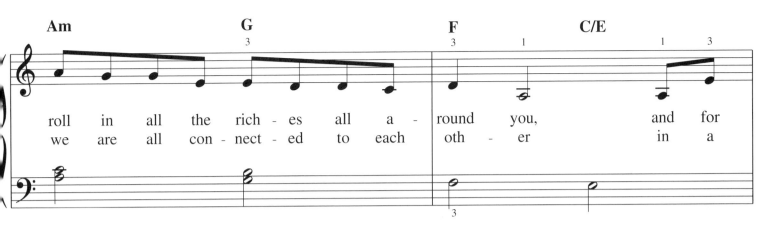

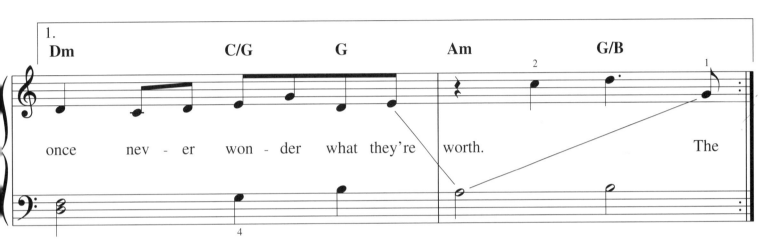

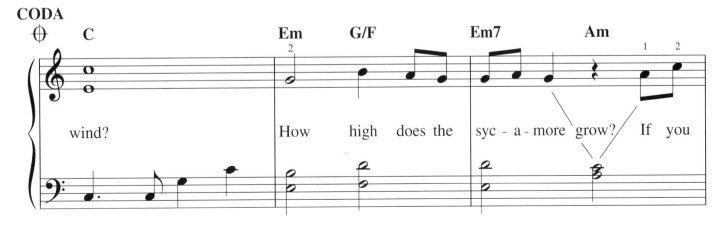

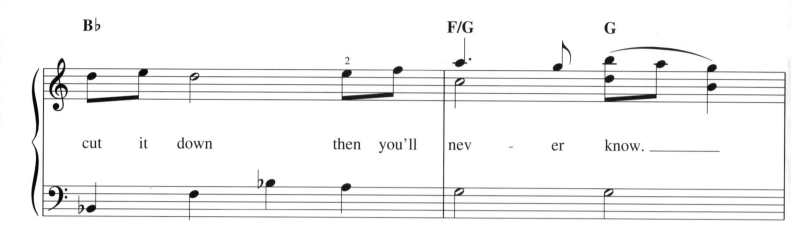

cut it down   then you'll   nev - er   know. _____

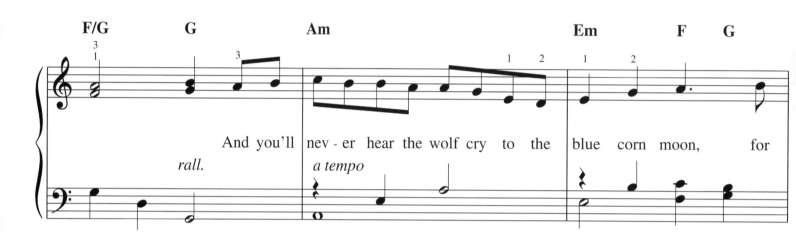

rall.   And you'll nev - er hear the wolf cry to the   blue corn moon,   for

a tempo

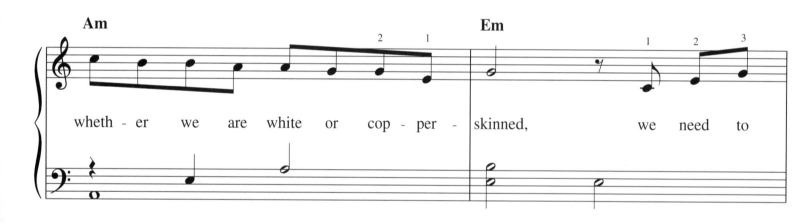

wheth - er   we   are white   or   cop - per - skinned,   we need to

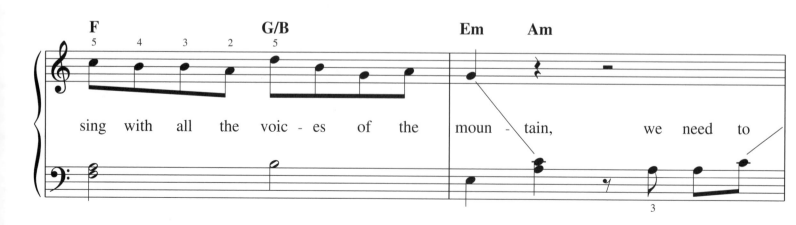

sing with all the voic - es of the   moun - tain,   we need to

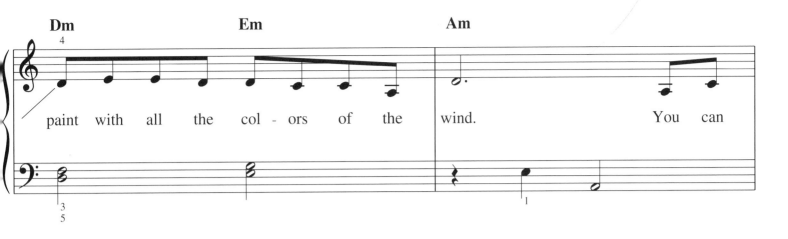

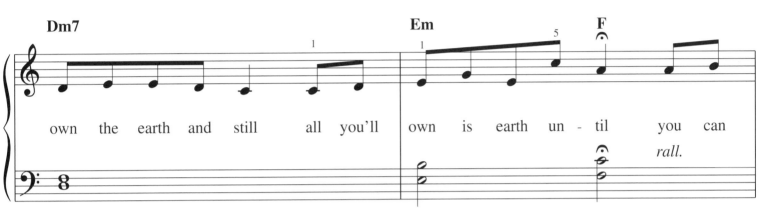

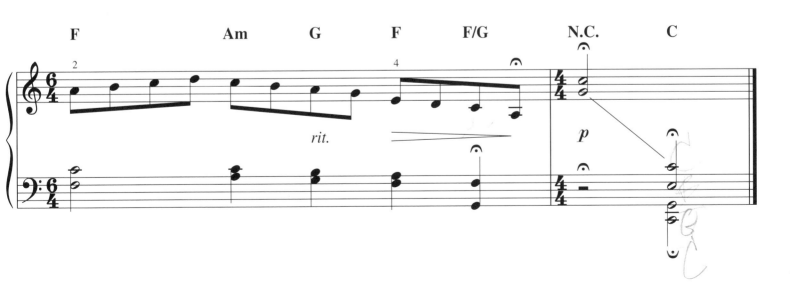

IF I NEVER KNEW YOU

(Love Theme from POCAHONTAS)
from Walt Disney's POCAHONTAS

Music by ALAN MENKEN
Lyrics by STEPHEN SCHWARTZ

Moderately

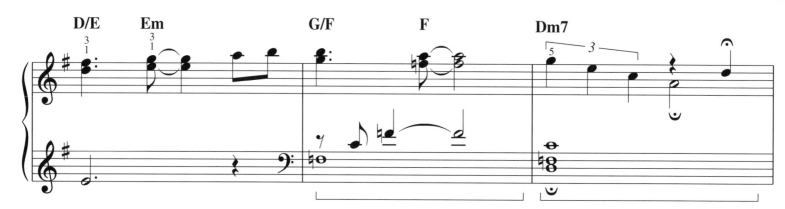

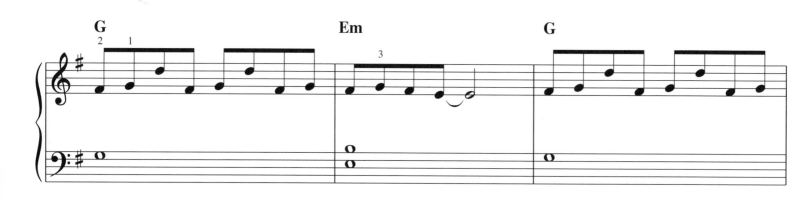

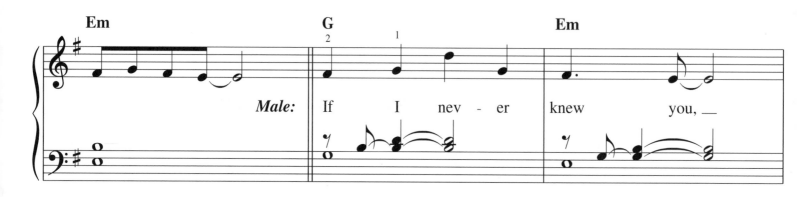

Male: If I nev - er knew you, ___

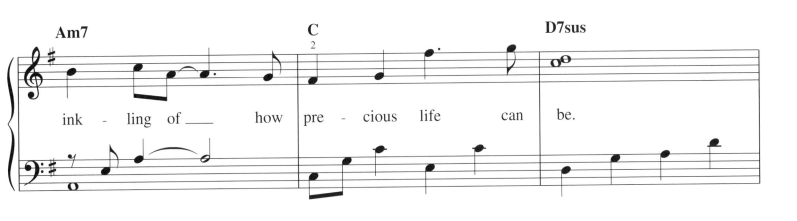

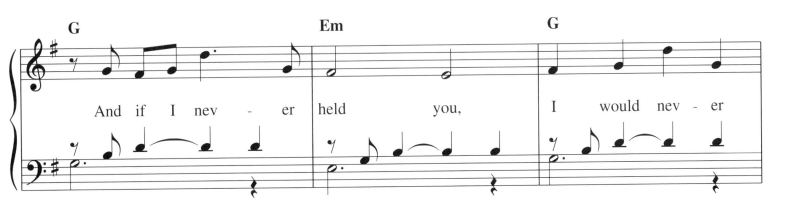

the miss-ing part of me. ____ In this world so

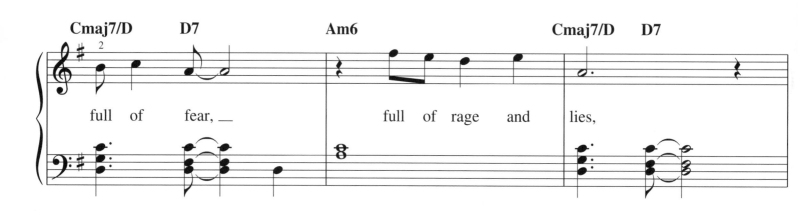

full of fear, __ full of rage and lies,

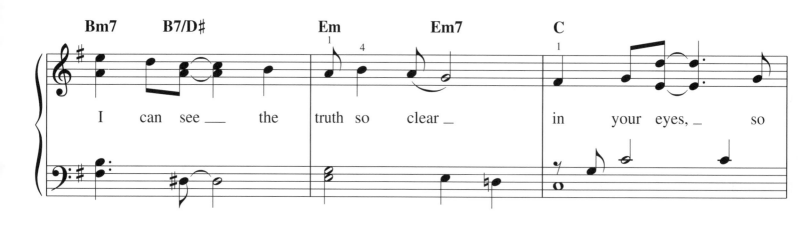

I can see __ the truth so clear __ in your eyes, __ so

dry your eyes. __ And I'm so grate - ful to you.

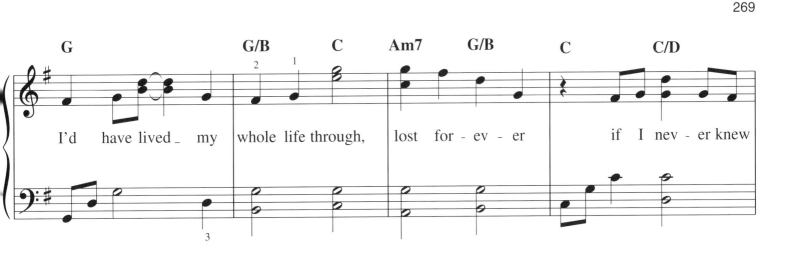

I'd have lived _ my whole life through, lost for-ev-er if I nev-er knew

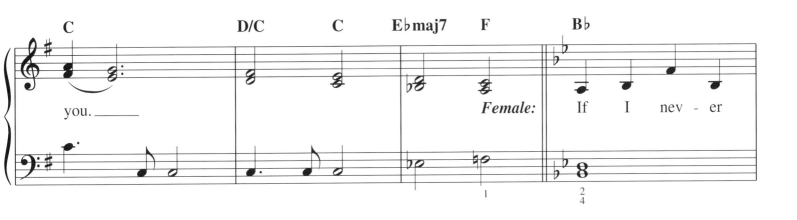

you. _____ *Female:* If I nev - er

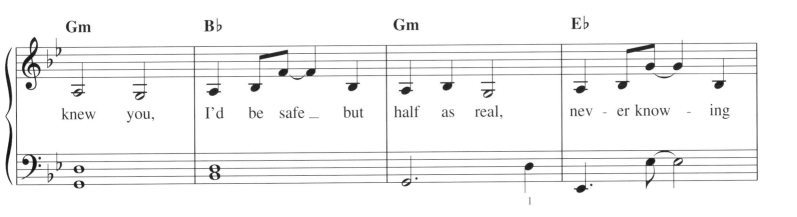

knew you, I'd be safe _ but half as real, nev-er know - ing

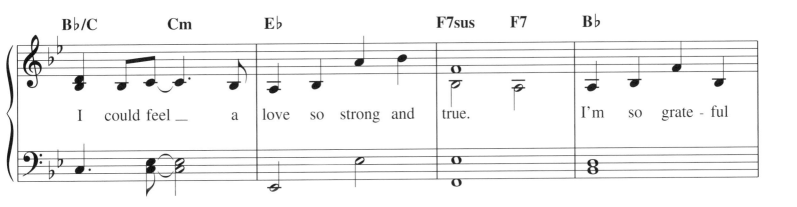

I could feel _ a love so strong and true. I'm so grate - ful

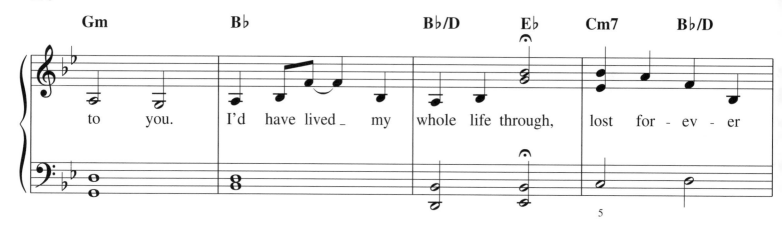

to you. I'd have lived_ my whole life through, lost for - ev - er

if I nev - er knew you.

Male: I thought our love would be so beau - ti - ful.

Female: Some - how we'd make the whole world bright._ *Both:* I nev - er knew that fear and

hate could be so strong, all they'd leave us were these whis-pers in the night, ___ but

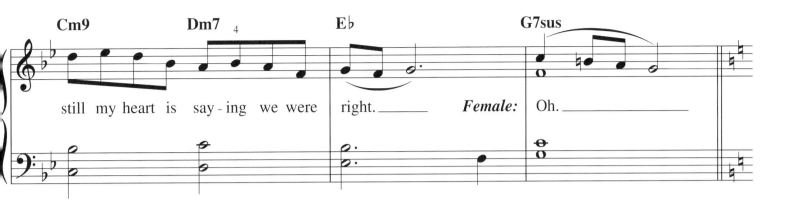

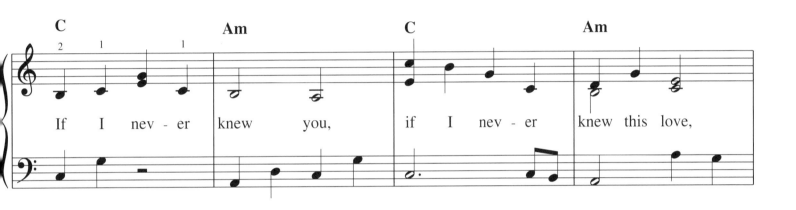

still my heart is say-ing we were right.____ **Female:** Oh.____

If I nev-er knew you, if I nev-er knew this love,

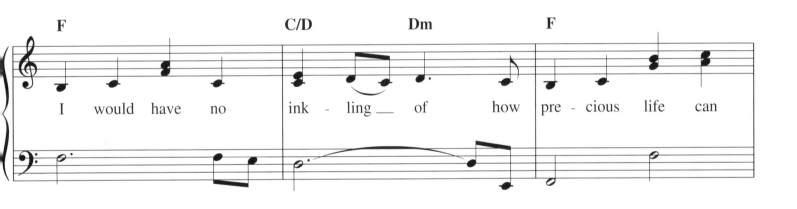

I would have no ink-ling __ of how pre-cious life can

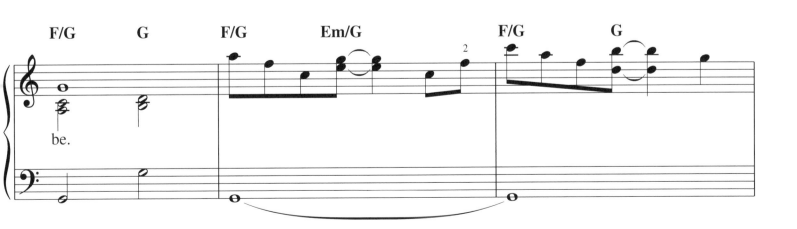

be.

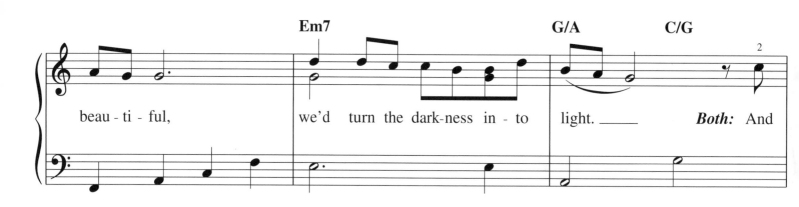

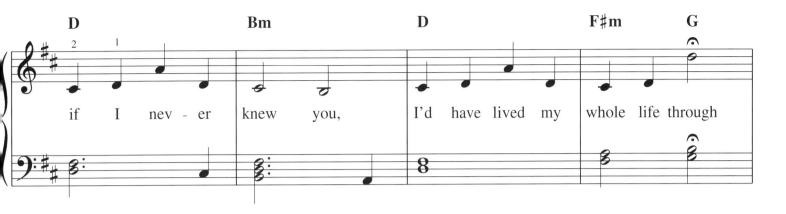

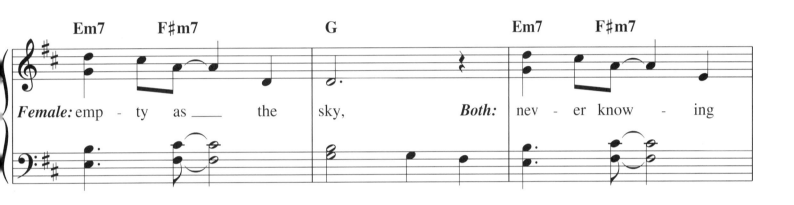

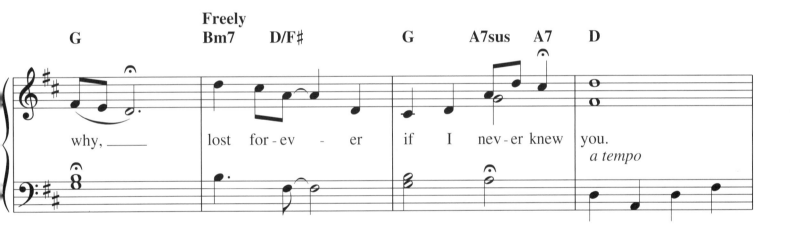

JUST AROUND THE RIVERBEND
from Walt Disney's POCAHONTAS

Music by ALAN MENKEN
Lyrics by STEPHEN SCHWARTZ

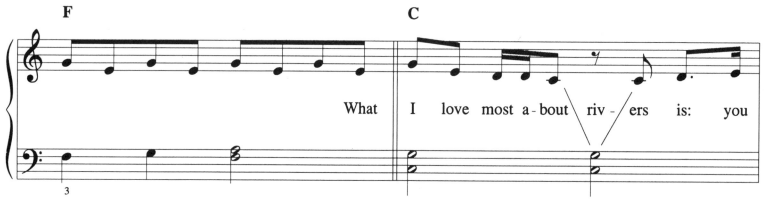

What I love most a-bout riv-ers is: you

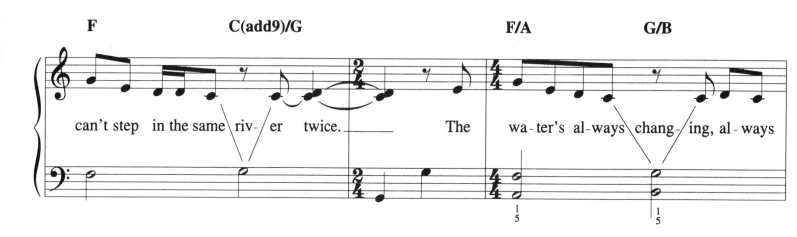

can't step in the same riv-er twice. ___ The wa-ter's al-ways chang-ing, al-ways

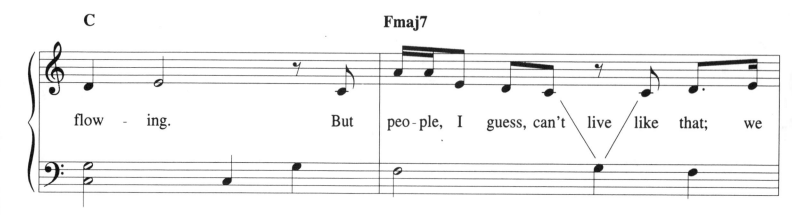

flow - ing. But peo-ple, I guess, can't live like that; we

all must pay a price: To be safe we lose our chance of ev - er

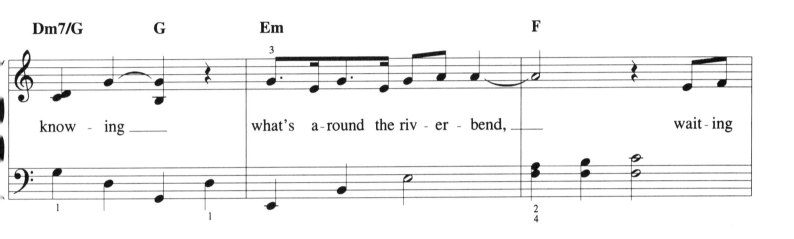

know - ing _____ what's a-round the riv - er - bend, _____ wait-ing

just a-round the riv - er - bend. I look once more

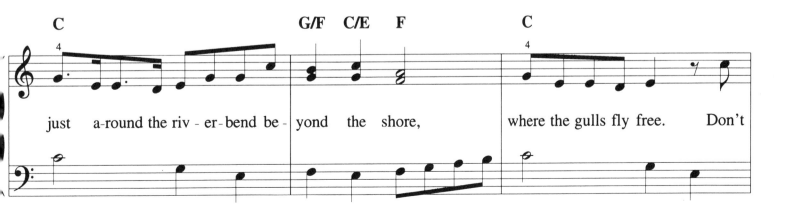

just a-round the riv - er-bend be - yond the shore, where the gulls fly free. Don't

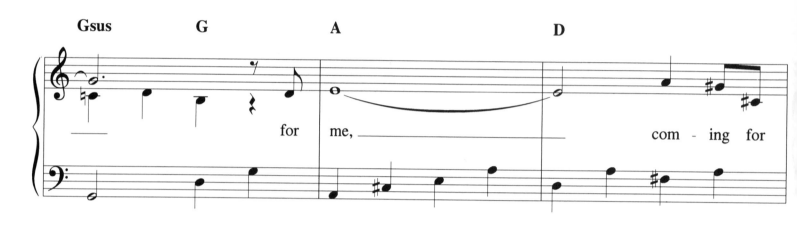

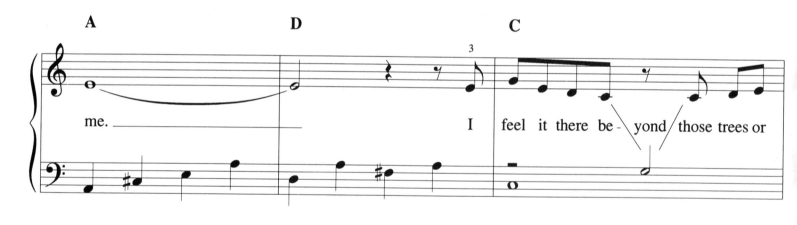

277

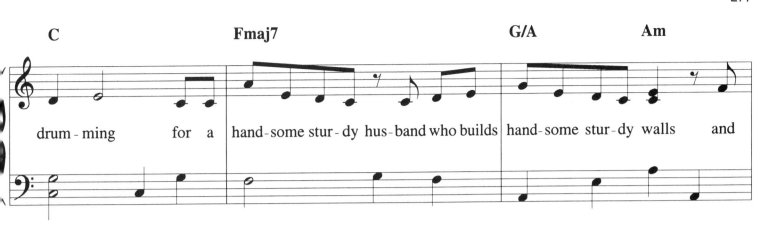

drum - ming for a hand-some stur - dy hus-band who builds hand-some stur-dy walls and

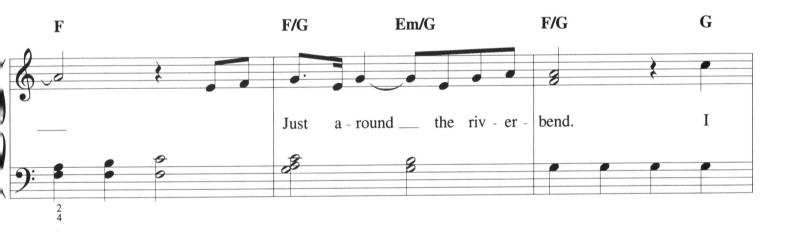

nev - er dreams that some-thing might be com - ing just a - round the riv - er - bend?

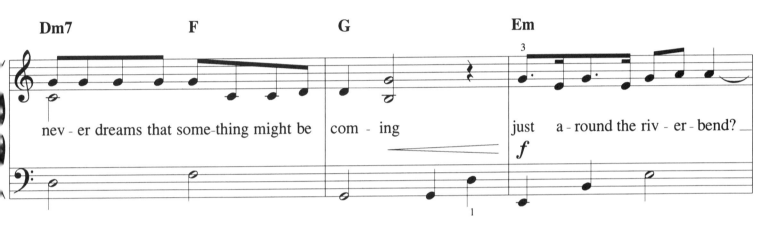

Just a - round ___ the riv - er - bend. I

look once more just a-round the riv - er-bend be - yond the shore,

C   **Am**   **D9sus**   **D9**

some-where past the sea.   Don't know what for...   why do all my dreams ex - tend

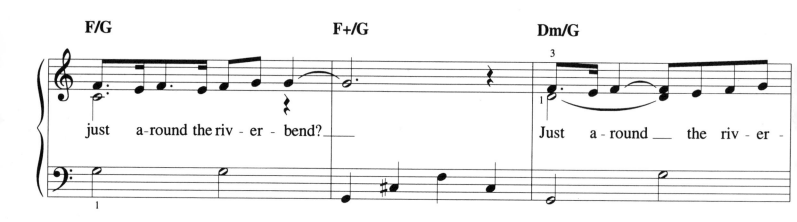

F/G   **F+/G**   **Dm/G**

just a-round the riv - er - bend?____   Just a - round ___ the riv - er -

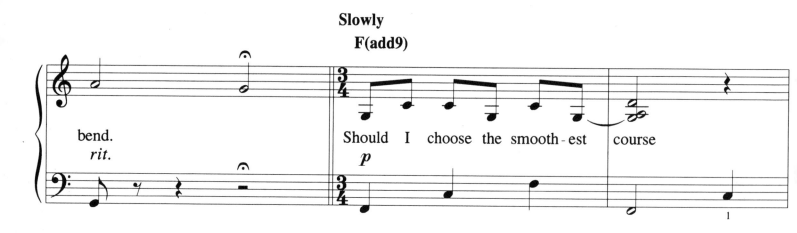

Slowly
F(add9)

bend.   Should I choose the smooth - est   course
rit.   *p*

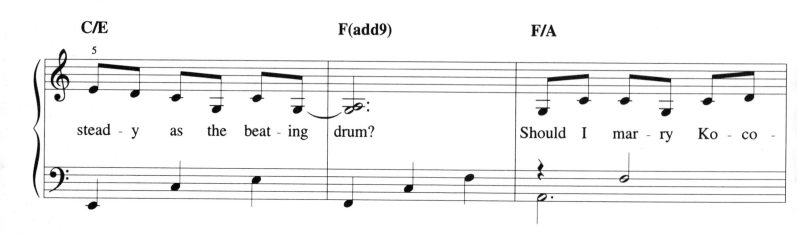

C/E   **F(add9)**   **F/A**

stead - y as the beat - ing drum?   Should I mar - ry Ko - co -

G/B   C   F(add9)

um?_____ Is all my dream-ing at an end? Or

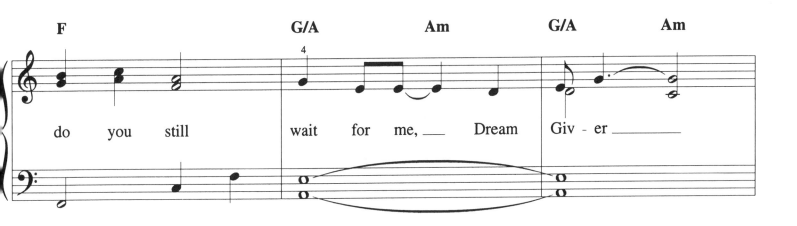

F   G/A   Am   G/A   Am

do you still wait for me, ___ Dream Giv - er _____

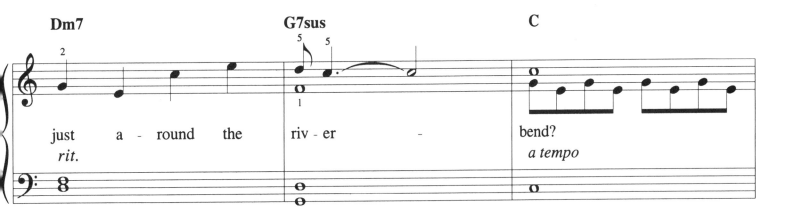

Dm7   G7sus   C

just a - round the riv - er - bend?

rit.   *a tempo*

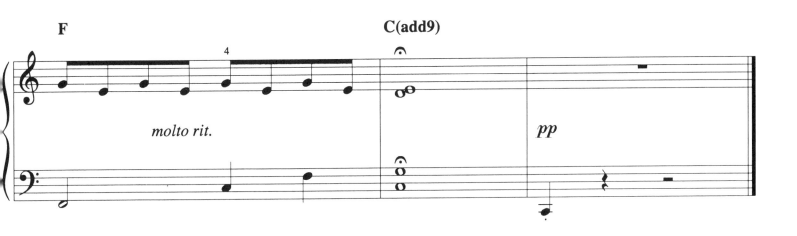

F   C(add9)

molto rit.   *pp*

STRANGERS LIKE ME

from Walt Disney Pictures' TARZAN™

Words and Music by
PHIL COLLINS

I wan-na know 'bout these stran - gers _ like _ me.

Tell me more; _

please show _ me.

Some-thing's fa - mil - iar 'bout these stran - gers _ like _ me.

mp Come with me now to see my world _____ where there's

beau - ty be - yond your dreams. Can you feel the things _ I

With pedal

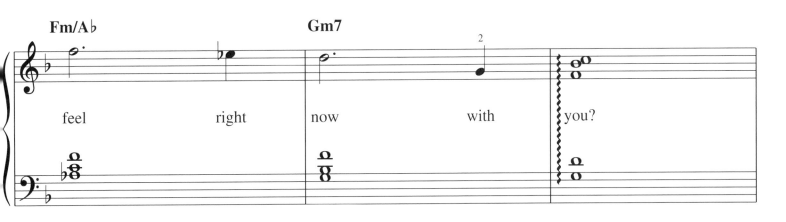

feel   right   now   with   you?

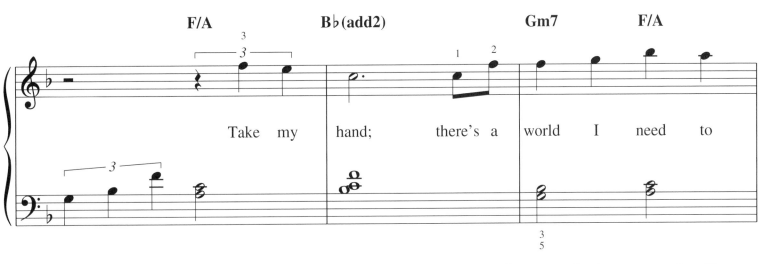

Take   my   hand;   there's a   world   I   need   to

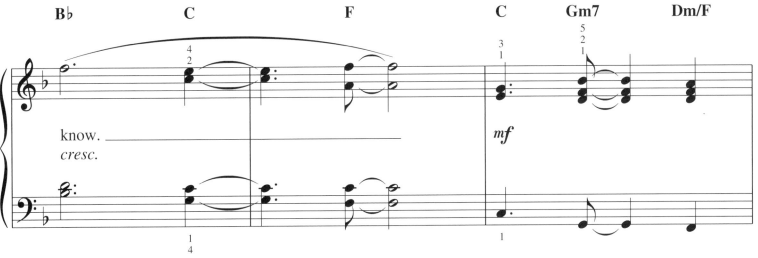

know.   *cresc.*   *mf*

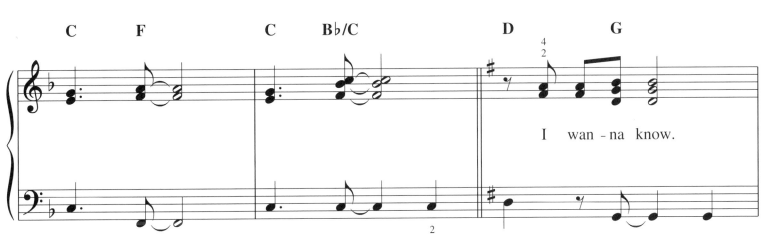

I   wan - na   know.

TWO WORLDS

from Walt Disney Pictures' TARZAN™

Words and Music by
PHIL COLLINS

Moderately

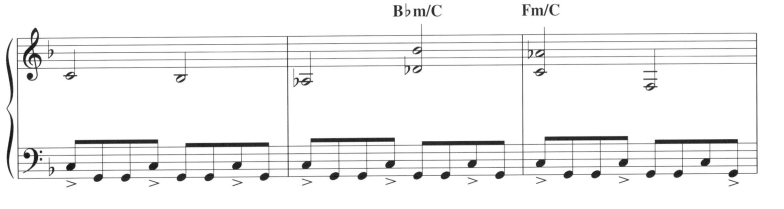

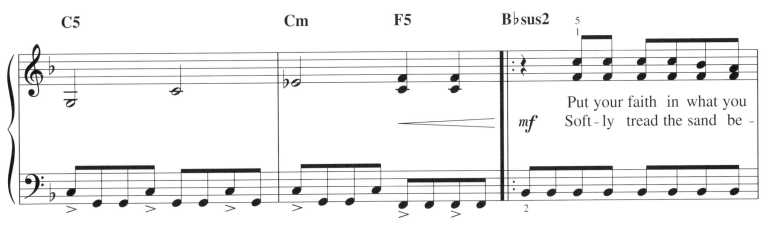

Put your faith in what you

Soft-ly tread the sand be -

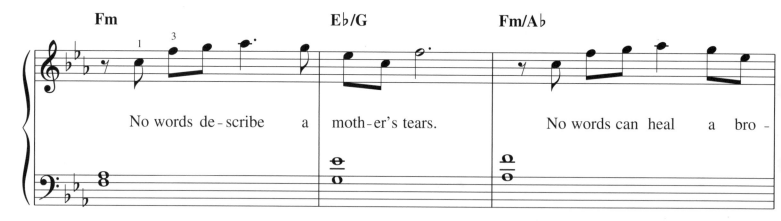

No words de-scribe a moth-er's tears. No words can heal a bro-

ken heart. A dream is gone; but where there's hope,

YOU'LL BE IN MY HEART

(Pop Version)
from Walt Disney Pictures' TARZAN™

Words and Music by
PHIL COLLINS

Moderately

Come stop your cry-ing; it will be all right. _

Just take my hand, hold it tight. _ I will pro-tect you from

all a - round _ you. I will be here; don't you cry.

For one so small you seem so strong. _
Why can't they un-der-stand the way we feel? ___

My arms will hold you, keep you safe and warm. _
They just don't trust _ what they can't ex - plain. _

This bond be-tween us
I know we're dif-f'rent, but

can't be bro - ken.
deep in - side _ us

I will be here; don't you cry.
we're not that dif - f'rent at all.

'Cause
And

With pedal

you'll be in my heart, yes, you'll be in my

294

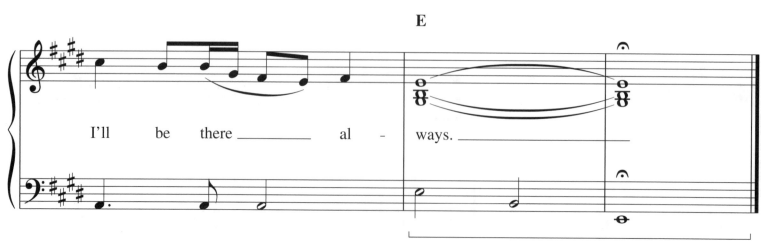

YOU'VE GOT A FRIEND IN ME

from Walt Disney's TOY STORY

Music and Lyrics by
RANDY NEWMAN

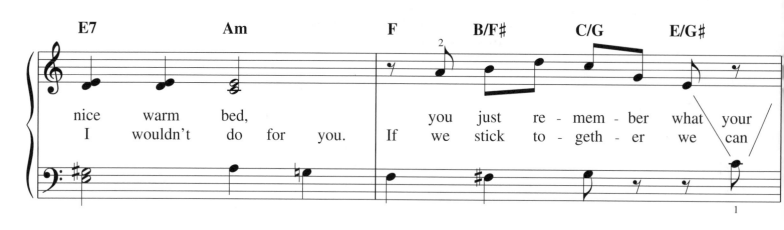

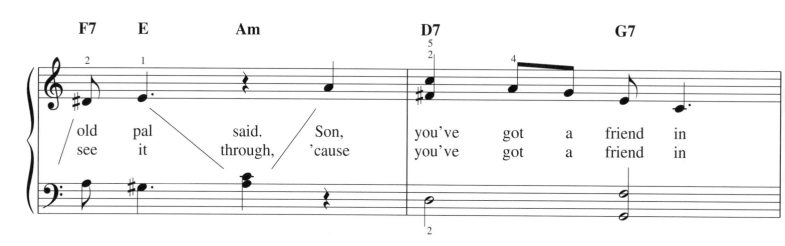

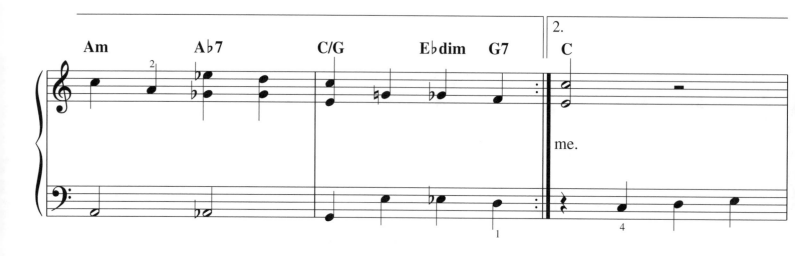

Now some oth - er folks might be a lit - tle bit smart - er than I am,

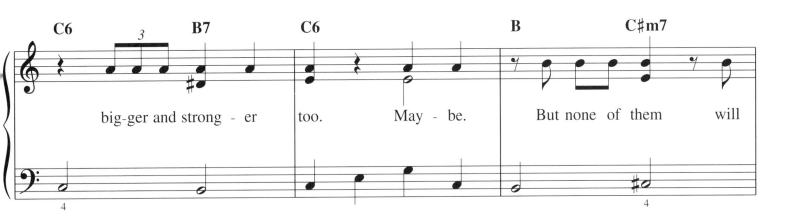

big-ger and strong - er too. May - be. But none of them will

ev - er love you the way I do, just me and you, __ boy.

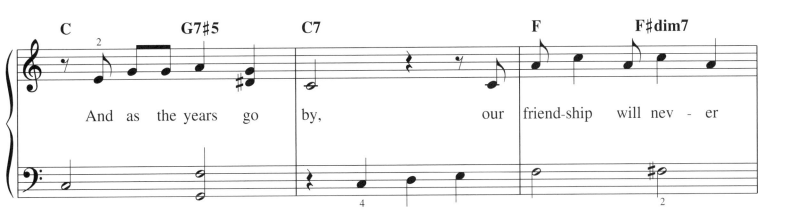

And as the years go by, our friend-ship will nev - er

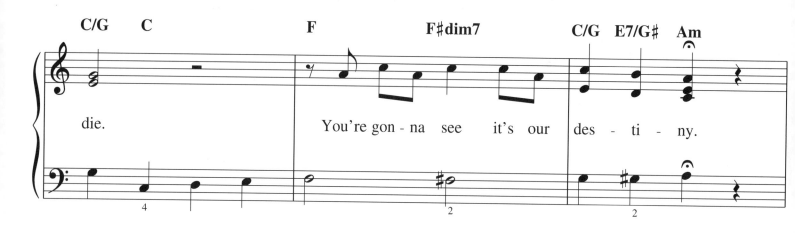

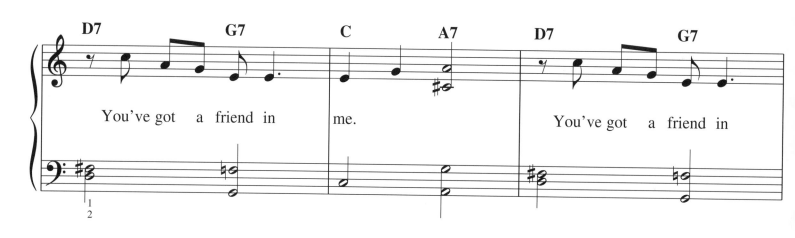

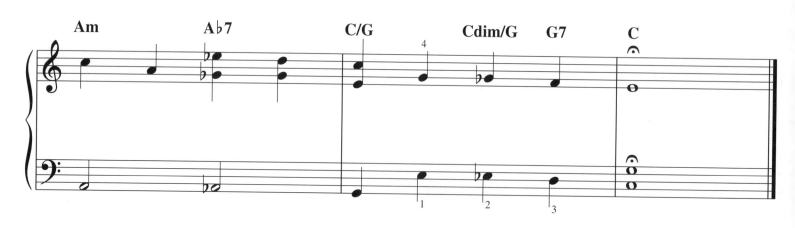

WHEN SHE LOVED ME

from Walt Disney Pictures' TOY STORY 2 - A Pixar Film

Music and Lyrics by
RANDY NEWMAN

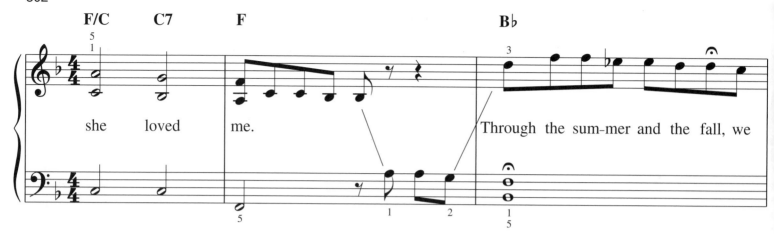

she loved me.
Through the sum-mer and the fall, we

had each oth-er, that was all. Just she and I to-geth-er, like it was meant to be.

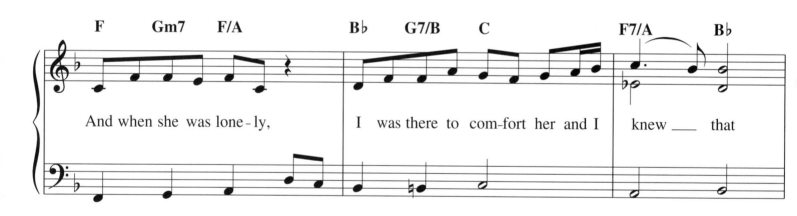

And when she was lone-ly, I was there to com-fort her and I knew ___ that

she loved me.

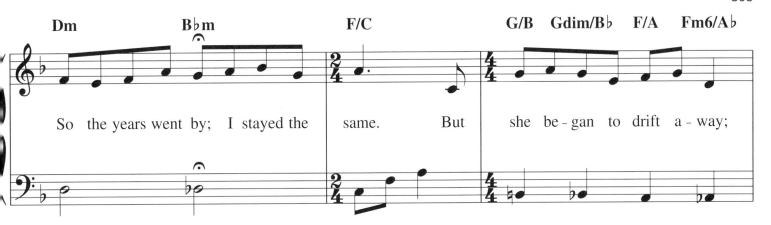

So the years went by; I stayed the same. But she be-gan to drift a-way;

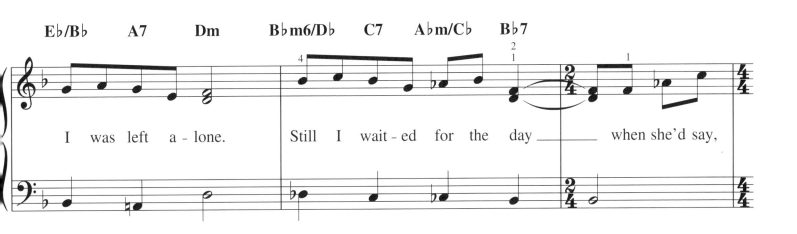

I was left a-lone. Still I wait-ed for the day _____ when she'd say,

"I will al-ways love you." Lone-ly and for-got-ten,

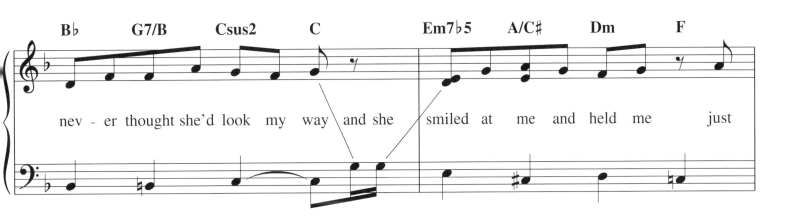

nev-er thought she'd look my way and she smiled at me and held me just

like she used to do   like she loved me   when she

loved me   When some-bod - y loved me,   ev - 'ry-thing was beau-ti-ful.

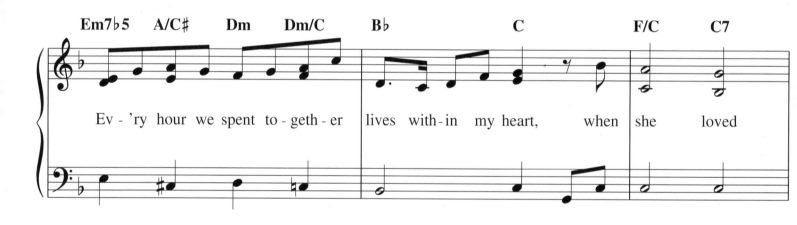

Ev - 'ry hour we spent to - geth - er   lives with-in my heart,   when she loved

me.